School for F.M. Alexander Studies
330 St. Georges Road
North Fitzroy,
VIC 3068
Phone: +61 3 9486 5900
www.alexanderschool.edu.au
e-mail: info@alexanderschool.edu.au
First published: November 2013
This edition: June 2017
Cover photo: A. Scarpa, "Sull' aneurisma", 1804

ATTMAP607A

Use Body Mapping to improve movement and posture

Study Manual
Learner Copy

Acknowledgements

Assessment Writer: Fiona Bryant
Instructional Designer: Fiona Bryant

Project mentor: David Moore

Version Number 2.1.

School for F. M. Alexander Studies
330 St. Georges Road, North Fitzroy, VIC 3068, Australia

National Course Code for Advanced Diploma of Alexander Technique Teaching
10403NAT
CRICOS Course Code 080908D- Einstein's Moon Pty Ltd
Provider Code for provision of training to overseas students is 02438J
(Einstein's Moon Pty Ltd)
Registered Training Organisation number 21278
Austudy Approved - Centrelink Institution Reference Number 3P330

Contents

SESSION INDEX CONTENT

Note: In addition to the material covered in these sessions all participants will receive a short individual Alexander technique lesson prior to each session.

Session	Part	Topic	Duration
ONE	One	*Introduction to Body Mapping*	
	Two	*Beginning to explore our Body Map*	
	Three	*The Atlanto-Occipital Joint & the Primary Control*	
	Four	*The Spine and Whole-Body Balance*	2 hours
	One	*The boney structures of respiration: Ribs and Spine*	
	Two	*The Organs of Respiration: Lungs*	
	Three	*The Muscles of Respiration: Intercostals, Diaphragm, Abdominal Wall and Pelvic Floor*	
	Four	*Mapping our language*	2 hours
THREE	One	*The Boney structure of the Upper Arm: Clavicle Scapula, Humerus and Joints*	
	Two	*The Boney structure of the Upper Arm: Scapula*	
	Three	*The Boney structure of the Upper Arm: Humerus*	2 hours
FOUR	One	*Elbow and Forearm bones*	
	Two	*The Wrist*	
	Three	*The Hand*	
	Four	*Putting it all together: The Whole Arm*	2 hours
FIVE	One	*Overview of the Leg*	
	Two	*The Pelvis*	
	Three	*Hip Joint and Upper Leg*	
	Four	*The Knee*	2 hours

Session	Part	Topic	Duration
SIX	One	*Lower Leg and Ankle*	
	Two	*The Foot*	
	Three	*Putting it all together: Footwear, Standing and Walking*	2 hours
SEVEN	One	*Balance is Posture, Posture is Balance: Re-mapping 'Posture'*	
	Two	*The Forgotten Senses: Kinesthesia and Proprioception*	
	Three	*An Obstacle: Faulty Sensory Appreciation*	2 hours
EIGHT	One	*Muscle Function*	
	Two	*Muscles Types and Imbalances*	
	Three	*Reflexes and restoration of muscular imbalance*	
	Four	*Mapping Muscles to understand and address specific mis-use*	2 hours
NINE	One	*Structures of the Skull: Cranium, Jaw, Tongue*	
	Two	*The Upper Spine and Internal Structures*	
	Three	*Review of respiration and connection to phonation*	
	Four	*Putting it together: mapping the spatial relationships of head and neck structures*	2 hours
TEN	One	*Internal Organs, Superficial Musculature and Referred Pain: an overview*	
	Two	*A New Map of You: Re-drawing and reviewing your Body Map*	
	Three	*Practical applications to workplace and other activities*	
	Four	*A review of Body Mapping processes and conclusions*	2-4 hours

Total Duration: 20-24 contact hours

PRE-SESSION STUDY REQUIREMENTS AND ASSESSMENT

BEFORE Sessions 2-10, you will be required to READ and COMPLETE this Study Manual including any note writing, drawing and explorations (where possible).

During the face-to-face session time there will be an opportunity to discuss the material in the Study Manual and ask questions on any aspects that were not clear.

The bulk of the face-to-face session time will then be devoted to more open experiential Body Mapping and Alexander Technique work as a large group.

For those undertaking the full teacher training course as well as guests, working on the Body Mapping Study Manual including the detailed practical explorations described within it, would be an ideal way to spend free time during 'turns' each morning. ❾ DISCUSS points may be good starting points for conversations with fellow trainees.

Please note that in addition to a short written exam, your Study Manual will be cited in order to assess your satisfactory completion of the unit, ATTMAP607A Use body mapping to improve movement and posture.

TERMINOLOGY & RECOMMENDED READING

Throughout this manual anatomical names i.e. clavicles are used primarily with common terms i.e. collarbones sometimes given in brackets. It is assumed learners undertaking this unit have prior knowledge of structural anatomy or are currently studying anatomy. The following texts are recommended reading for this unit:

- **The Anatomy Colouring Book** (Kapit W., Elson L.M., USA, Benjamin Cummings Publishers, 2002.) – for those who are still consolidating their structural anatomy knowledge

- **Anatomy of Movement** (Calais-Germain, Blandine. Seattle, Eastland Press, 1999.)

- **Anatomy of the Moving Body: A Basic Course in Bones, Muscles and Joints** (Dimon, Theodore Jr. California, North Atlantic Books, 2008.)

- **Body in Motion: Its Evolution and Design** (Dimon, Theodore Jr. California, North Atlantic Books 2011)

- **Use of the Self** (Alexander, F.M., (1931) Orion, UK, 2001)

KEY

The following symbols are used throughout this manual:

Symbol	Notes
▤ DRAW/LABEL/WRITE	*Use additional paper as required*
❾ DISCUSS	*If working alone, think and write about the proposed ideas*
☞ EXPLORE	*Always read instructions carefully and seek advice from trainer if unsure*
▢ RECALL	*Refer back to previous sessions as required*
ⓘ IMPORTANT INFORMATION	*Important for relevance to profession and personal wellbeing*
® READING REQUIRED	*Details of books referred to throughout the manual are listed in the Bibliography. Your trainer can assist you to borrow or purchase texts as needed.*
↵ LATER	*This area will be covered in a later session or own time.*

EQUIPMENT

Learners will need:

- ✓ Note book for writing and drawing
- ✓ Access to anatomy text books/internet
- ✓ Comfortable clothing that they can move in i.e. track pants and top (not skirt)
- ✓ May also bring in items related to their profession i.e. musical instrument to use in practical explorations

SESSION ONE

Part One: Introduction to Body Mapping

What is Body Mapping?

Body Map is the term given to the representational map of our bodies we have each developed in our brains. It may also be called body model, body scheme or internal representation. In the first three years of our lives the development of our body map enables us to begin to walk, run, jump and speak. As we continue to grow and develop, so too does our body map. This process of development is predominantly informed by our experiences living in the world.

Unfortunately, over time our body maps tend to develop faults and entirely 'blank', unmapped areas. For example, when asked to point to their hip joints, many adults will point to a variety of areas within the pelvis and upper leg region. In general, the hip joint tends to be mapped higher and wider than its actual location. (The boney prominence of the iliac crest is easy to palpate and often mistaken as the hip joint).

Why is correcting and refining my Body Map important?

If there is a disparity in the mental representation (body map) and the anatomical reality, the mental always wins in movement! In other words, the problem with a faulty or incomplete body map is that it directly and in this case negatively, informs the way we move. Our faulty or incomplete body map may cause us to move in ways that are awkward, injurious and painful because we are simply not moving according to our design.

In the cited example of mis-mapped hip joints, the likely consequence will be that when this person bends i.e. to pick something up, they bend from where they have mapped their hip joint rather than at the actual joint. This will mean that they will bend by flexing the lumbar spine, placing sudden stress and load through an area that is not designed to repeatedly perform such action. Over time this can lead to pain and injury.

What is the Alexander Technique and how does it relate to Body Mapping?

The Alexander technique is based upon the discovery by Frederick Matthias Alexander, a professional actor, who in spite of his best endeavors was unable to change faulty patterns of movement which were responsible for him losing his voice. His key finding was that even after identifying what it was he was doing with himself and what it was that he should and wanted to be doing instead, his kinesthetic[3] judgment of that which he was doing was faulty. His sense of feeling was quite entirely unreliable.

---

[3] Kinethesia- A sense mediated by receptors located in muscles, tendons, and joints and stimulated by bodily movements and tensions; *also* : sensory experience derived from this sense

He reflected, "If ever anyone was at an impasse it was I. For here I was, faced with the fact that my feeling, the only guide I had to depend on for the direction of my use, was untrustworthy." However he didn't give up at this point. "'Surely' I agued ' if it is possible for feeling to become untrustworthy as a means of direction, it should also be possible to make it trustworthy again.'"[4]

And indeed he succeeded. A course of Alexander Technique lessons are aimed at re-educating our kinesthetic and proprioceptive[5] senses so that we can indeed do with our minds and bodies what we intend to do.

Body mapping is not a replacement for Alexander technique lessons, but an important complement. When errors in body mapping (false ideas about where parts of our bodies are located, what sort of movements they can perform and how we should effectively engage them) are added to faulty kinestheic and proprioceptive awareness, any attempt to make useful changes to posture and movement will be ineffective and will not last.

How does Body Mapping support and enhance my learning of the Alexander Technique?

A detailed and accurate body map will enhance the study of all somatic based education methods including Alexander Technique, Feldenkrais, Yoga, Pilates, Tai Chi and Chi Gong. By engaging in the process of continually correcting and refining your body map you will find you are more effectively able to utilize the information received in the process of learning Alexander Technique.

▤   WRITE a short summary (no more than a few sentences) describing (a) what a body map is, (b) why it is important and (c) how you believe it relates to your profession:

---

[4] Alexander, F.M. *Use of the Self,* London, Orion Books, 2001, p. 36.
[5] Proprioception - Perception of stimuli relating to position, posture, equilibrium, or internal condition.

Part Two

Beginning to explore our Body Map

▤   DRAW a Map/Diagram of your body on the page provided or in your notebook.

ⓘ This activity is not a test! Your drawing will provide an invaluable reference point as you work through the unit. It will very quickly inform you about those areas of your body map that are clear as well as those that aren't. It will be of most benefit to include the skeletal structure (as much as you know) in your drawing since this unit looks primarily at the mapping of bones and joints.

* If you feel unable to draw from scratch, you may like to label to body outline also provided in this booklet. Simply draw and label as much detail as you can.

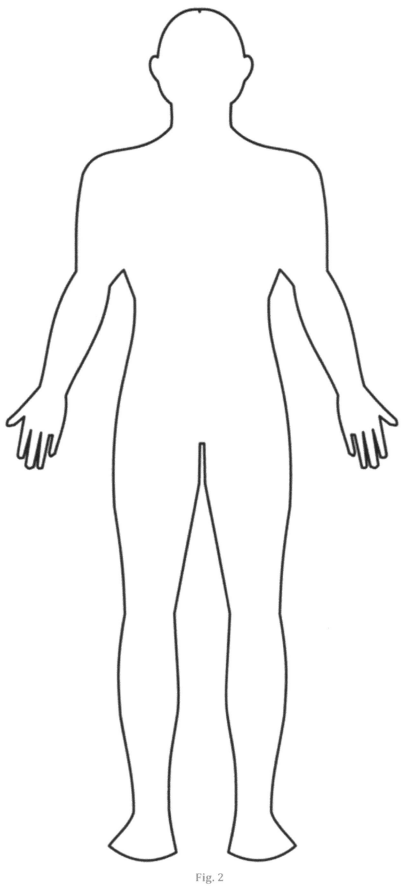

Fig. 2

❾ DISCUSS

What did you observe as you did this activity? What parts of your map are blank or unclear?

Have a look at these pictures. What do you see? What do you think is inaccurate or missing?

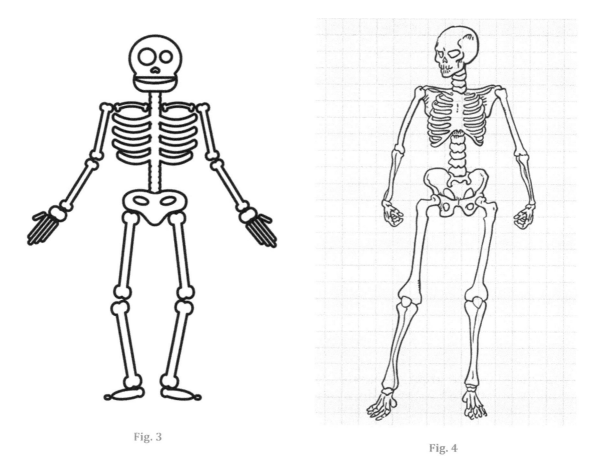

Fig. 3

Fig. 4

Correcting your body map (structural, functional, size errors) is an ongoing process. It can involve the following activities, all of which will be covered in the ten sessions of this unit:

- ✓ Drawing
- ✓ Asking Questions i.e. where are my lungs?
- ✓ Looking at anatomical images (books, internet)
- ✓ Palpating (touch)
- ✓ Imitation (observing those who move well- babies, some elite sports people, dancers, martial artists)
- ✓ Looking in the mirror
- ✓ Constructive rest/semi supine (conscious constructive thinking, imagining, visualizing)
- ✓ Lessons with an Alexander technique teacher

We move in the way in which we think we are constructed (consciously or unconsciously).

Part Three

The Atlanto-Occipital Joint and Primary Control

❾ DISCUSS

Let's begin by looking at a commonly un-mapped or mis-mapped, but very important area of the body – where the head meets the spine. How did you draw this area in your picture? How would you point to or touch this area?

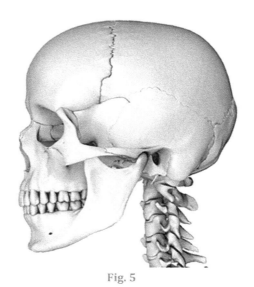

Fig. 5

What might be the impact of correctly mapping this area? Do you have a sense of just how much the head weighs? How do we go about re-mapping this area?

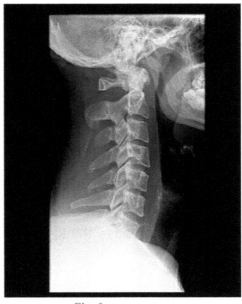

Fig. 6

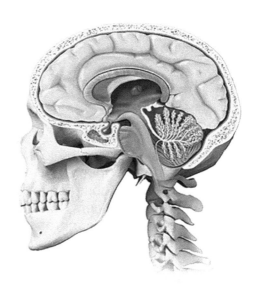

Fig. 7

∝ EXPLORE
Look at the top cervical vertebra – the atlas, on which the head sits. Also look at the axis with which the atlas articulates. The joint of the head and atlas is called the atlanto-occipital (AO) joint. You move at this joint when you do a careful 'yes' nodding motion of the head. The joint of the atlas and axis is called the atlanto-axial (AA) joint. This joint can be felt when we do a 'no' nodding motion of the head. It is important to understand that no rotation occurs at the AO joint, but rather this happens at the lower AA joint.

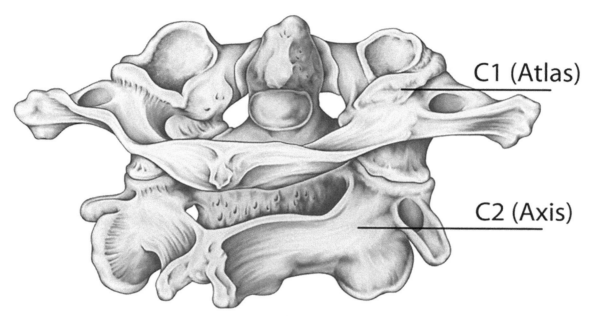

C1 (Atlas)

C2 (Axis)

Fig. 8

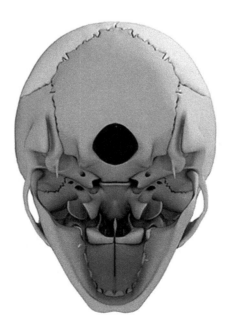

Fig. 9

cs EXPLORE

Pass around the 5 kg sandbag, appreciating that this represents the weight of the average human head (4.5 – 5kg) . It tends to be surprisingly heavy to most people.

You can learn to free the joint of your head and spine so that your head balances beautifully!

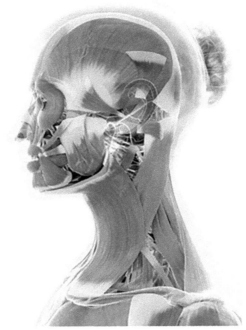

Fig. 10

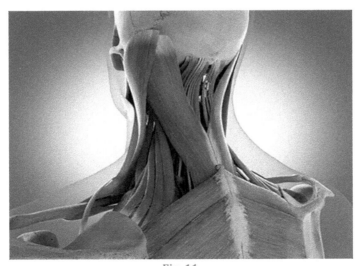

Fig. 11

Notice the mass of long, round, deep and powerful muscles situated at the neck to support and connect the head to the spine and torso.

cs EXPLORE
Sitting or standing, tense you neck and shoulders and observe how this feels both at your neck and in general through the rest of your body. Now let go of this tension and imagine the head delicately balanced on top of your spine at your newly mapped joint. This joint is called the atlanto-occipital as it is the meeting of the atlas of the cervical spine and the occiput bone of the head.

❾ DISCUSS
What did you notice during this exploration? Could you detect a correlation between a tense neck and balance at the atlanto-occipital joint?

Freeing your neck is the key to re-balancing thus freeing the whole of you.

cs EXPLORE in pairs HOW we free our neck and HOW this impacts upon movements of the head.

One person stands behind the other and gently puts their hands on the neck. This person makes a request to their partner, "*don't* allow me to turn your head." The partner doesn't allow their head to be turned. Next, the request is made, "*do* allow me to turn your head." The partner allows the head to be moved. Swap over role and repeat.

Fig. 12

❾ DISCUSS
HOW did the person having their head moved stop this movement and then allow it (i.e. what did they think or do?)

Merely thinking creates activity in the brain without adding to physical tension. We can actually change our posture and the entire way we use ourselves with our <u>thoughts</u>.[6]

❾ DISCUSS
Why might it be important to recognize and thus address ourselves as a whole person rather than in separate (i.e. mental, physical, emotional) parts?

How do you currently think about yourself? You may find you can evidence this in the way you speak about yourself.

The primary cause of poor posture is over-tightening of the powerful neck muscle. When tightened these muscles pull the head off balance, in turn negatively affecting the whole body balance.

Fig. 13

Fig. 14

Alexander termed the dynamic, relational balance of the head, neck and back (torso) the **Primary Control**. Primary aptly indicates a hierarchy that exists – that this balance sets up or furnishes the queue for balance throughout the rest of the body. Our priority is therefore to consciously attend to the process of freeing our necks, so that good Primary Control can be established and sustained.

---

[6] Brennan, Richard. *Change Your Posture, Change Your Life: How the power of the Alexander Technique can combat back pain, tension and stress*, London, Watkins Publishing, 2012, p. 134.

Fig. 15

In order to establish and sustain this Primary Control, Alexander evolved a set of **"directions"** or mental orders that we project. Throughout all of the ensuing sessions, you will be reminded to project these directions before and during any activity or exploration.

୯ଞ EXPLORE Come into standing mentally (or even verbally to begin with) projecting the following sequence of the Alexander Directions:

- Allow the neck to be free *so that*
- the head can go forward and up *so that*
- the back (whole torso) can lengthen and widen

Repeat this a few times, and observe any changes (they may be subtle) that you notice is your whole self. It is important to trust that this process will elicit a subtle change and that you must resist temptation to try to 'do' these directions in a physical way.

Alexander developed this process of projecting the directions for the Primary Control in order to offset and even prevent the habits of discoordination he found that he brought to virtually all activity. The premise of this process, of engaging a mental process in order to direct the physical, is founded in Alexander's insistence that we are whole, or a **psychophysical** unity as he described it.

↵ LATER
In your daily life, you can begin to give the Alexander directions and observe what changes this elicits. Standing, walking, driving, talking on the phone, sitting at a computer are all examples of activities within which you can start to project your directions.

Here they are again:

- Allow the neck to be free *so that*
- the head can go forward and up *so that*
- the back (whole torso) can lengthen and widen

When giving mental orders or directions, you are directly influencing the entire way you use yourself (operate), including your posture, whether you 'feel' anything happening or not.[7]

® READING REQUIRED
In your own time, it is recommended that you read Chapter One: Evolution of a technique in Alexander's *Use of the Self,* London, Orion Books, 2001. Here Alexander describes the evolution of the technique including these directions.

Part Four

The Spine and Whole-Body Balance

Look back at your earlier drawing. How did you draw your spine? In particular, does it have curves? How many vertebrae did you draw? Now have a close look at the skeleton. Count the vertebra and note the direction of the curves.

The spine that supports your mobile, balanced head is curvy (not straight) and in this way can absorb impact so we can run and jump and not get injured!

Fig. 16

Fig. 17

---

[7] Brennan, Richard. *Change Your Posture, Change Your Life: How the power of the Alexander Technique can combat back pain, tension and stress*, London, Watkins Publishing, 2012, p. 134.

▤ DRAW a curved line representing the spine here including the new details you have just gathered.

❾ DISCUSS and ℭঽ EXPLORE the way in which common ideas of 'good posture' may do more harm than good and the impact upon the spinal curves. Using the mirror begin now to look at what happens when we adopt 'bad posture' and also 'good posture' in particular noting the exaggeration and flattening of the spinal curves.

ⓘ IMPORTANT
Using the mirror
From here on, you will be encouraged to work in pairs and using a mirror or mirrors in any explorations you do. The use of the mirrors is very important if we are to gain an accurate picture of our habitual patterns of use or organisation in all activities. Alexander used a combination of 3 strategically organized mirrors in order to see with great detail what he was doing with himself. He came to rely on the feedback of the mirrors as very early in his experiments he discovered his feeling of what he was doing was immensely inaccurate and thus untrustworthy. We will cover this phenomenon in more detail during Session Seven. For now, you can simply begin to SEE yourself in the mirror and work to do so in a constructive manner i.e. Not getting distracted by irrelevant aspects of appearance or critical self-talk. Remember it offers a wonderfully objective source of feedback.

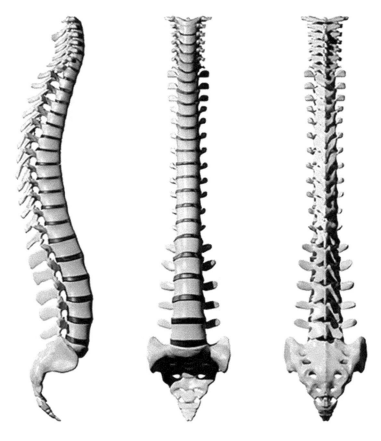

Fig. 18

☐ RECALL and ❾ DISCUSS what we have learned about how the head is balanced atop the spine at the atlanto-occipital joint. How might the curves of the spine be affected if the head is off balance?

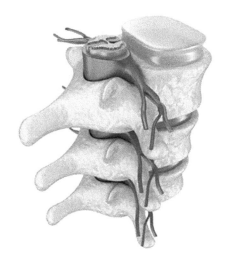

Fig. 19

30

☰ DRAW another picture of your spine below. This time we are looking at how you consider your spine in relation to the line of gravity[8] through the body. In other words, from the side, how are the curves distributed.

TOP OF SPINE

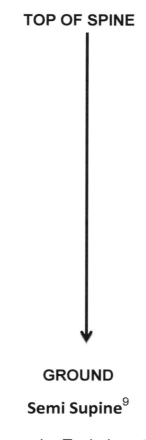

GROUND

Semi Supine[9]

One procedure used in the Alexander Technique to support you to become more aware of yourself, in particular tension, is laying in Semi Supine.

ⓘ IMPORTANT
If you have back pain or any pain that you know is made worse when you lay on your back you will need to ask your trainer for help. The trainer will probably be able to help you by slightly altering your body alignment, by the use of props or by finding you an alternative position. You may find you are able to perform this procedure on your side or in prone and you will be advised accordingly.

This procedure is a highly constructive way of beginning to reduce tension you are holding by way of consciously directing and projecting your thoughts in a supported resting position. If done regularly (10- 20min each day is highly advisable) it can help to align and elongate the spine and improve overall posture.

---

[8] In the human body that is stood in anatomical position the line of gravity runs like a plumb line from head to toe passing through the middle of the body and through the centre of gravity to the base of support. In an inanimate object the line of gravity is defined as "an imaginary line that extends from the centre of gravity to the base of support. The centre of gravity is defined as "that point in a body or system around which it's mass or weight is evenly distributed or balanced and through which the force of gravity acts.

[9] For step by step instructions and pictures, you can also refer to Chris Raff's, *Introducing the Alexander Technique*, Australia, Axiom, 2011.

Fig. 20

It is easier to let go of tension when lying down because gravity is working on your body in a different way and there are fewer balance issues and distractions to contend with. (Richard Brennan)

Benefits of Semi Supine Procedure[10]

✓ Improves overall organization/alignment
✓ Gives the intervertebral discs a chance to rehydrate which will result in increased height/length through spine
✓ Elongates any curves of the spine that have been exaggerated through compression (you are not aiming to straighten/flatten out the natural curves of the spine)
✓ Releases muscular tension and holding throughout the body
✓ Improves breathing (capacity and coordination)
✓ Improves circulation (blood flows better when there is less tension in the musculature)
✓ Lessens pressure on nerves, especially if there is an impingement condition present
✓ Allows the internal organs to move, reorganize and function more effectively
✓ Assists overall energy levels through the resting of the musculature and nervous system
✓ Can offer reduction in emotional disturbances such as stress, anxiety through combined physical and mental rebalancing

❀ EXPLORE
To experience the Semi Supine procedure, your trainer will now guide you through it along the lines of the following description. You can use this description to refer back to.

---

[10] Adapted from Brennan, Richard. *Change Your Posture, Change Your Life: How the power of the Alexander Technique can combat back pain, tension and stress*, London, Watkins Publishing, 2012, p. 156.

32

SEMI SUPINE

Take some books (approx. 2-3 novels) for under your head and find a place to lie on your back on the floor. In the first session the trainer will check on the exact height of books which you require.

Make sure you are warm and if needed use a yoga mat.

Once on your back, bend your knees up and have the feet flat on the floor.
Rest your hands on your torso or by your sides.

To check the height of your books you will need to become aware of how your neck feels. If you feel squashed through the throat area you may have too many books. If it feels like the back of your neck is tense or the head is dropping back you may not have enough books. Once you have this organized, direct your thoughts to releasing the weight of the head to rest on the books.

The soles of your feet are flat on the floor and with even weight distribution.
The knees are pointed to the ceiling.

If the legs are tending to fall inwards, you can try having your feet closer together. If they are falling outward, you can try having the feet further apart.

The back is resting into the floor but you are not pushing it or trying to flatten out the natural curves.

The arms are relaxed and there is a sense of breadth through the shoulders and chest area (again without pushing).

The pelvis is resting and echoes this sense of breadth and expansion.
Breathing is normal, preferable with the lips lightly closed, thus through the nose.

As you lay here, you want to stay awake (keep the eyes open) and active with your thinking. To begin with you may like to experiment with different approaches to how you direct your thinking during this time. Initially you will do well to keep coming back to the things that have just been described, in combination with noticing and letting go of any tension through the body. You may find that initially it is challenging to stay present with this process and that you are easily distracted with unrelated thoughts.

When you are ready to get up, you want to be very attentive to this process. In particular, you need to avoid lifting your head and tensing the neck and abdominal muscles. Rather, you want to roll your head and knees to the side to bring you to rest on your side. From here you can use your hand to push you to sit up, rather than tensing your neck muscles. To stand, you can come through a lunge or a squat, again paying special attention to any tensing of the neck muscles.

ⓘ IMPORTANT

It is important to understand that the benefits and your understanding of these benefits from laying in Semi Supine, will only arise when done on a regularly basis, ideally every day. While you will feel some immediate affects (at the time and straight afterwards), over a longer period of time you will really notice some profound changes.

Fig. 21

▤ DRAW another picture of your spine below, this time as it is when you lay down in the semi supine position you have just experienced. You may like to draw some arrows ⬇ ⬇ ⬇ to indicate the force of gravity in relation to the spine in this orientation.

SESSION TWO

Part One

The boney structures of respiration: Ribs and Spine

❾ DISCUSS
What boney structures are directly connected to the spine?
Look back at your drawing from Session One. How did your draw your ribs? How many are there? How are they attached?

There are **Twenty Four Ribs** and each one makes a joint with a process of the thoracic vertebra of the spine.

▭ RECALL
The Thoracic region of your spine including its curved shape from Session One. Twenty of the Ribs attach to cartilage in front. The four that don't attach in the front are known as the 'floating' ribs.

ⓘ IMPORTANT
Rib 'Cage' is an inaccurate and problematic description/image of the ribs. Each rib joins at the back (costo-vertebral joint) and front (costocartilage), is individual and mobile.

The ribs are wonderfully mobile and movement occurs at the joints in all our waking and sleeping hours – because we are breathing! On inhalation all the ribs move up and out, on exhalation all the ribs move down and in. This motion of the ribs is referred to as Excursion.

ଓ EXPLORE
Palpate your sternum; trace your ribs including the floating ribs.

On this picture number the ribs on one side 1-12. Then, use some arrows to indicate the movement direction of the ribs on Inhalation and then on Exhalation.

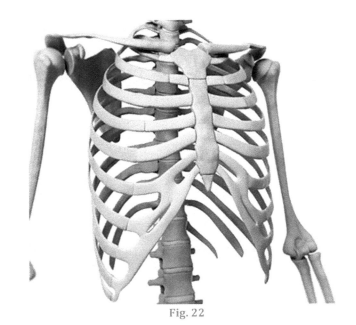

Fig. 22

ඏ EXPLORE

Work in pairs. One person stands behind partner and puts hands on lower ribs (back and sides). Both breathe normally and the person with his or her hands on observes the direction and range of motion. Swap over.

Then, try again this time purposely tightening the neck and compressing through spine. Notice how the movement is affected.

☐ RECALL and project the Alexander Directions from Session One:

- Allow the neck to be free *so that*
- the head can go forward and up *so that*
- the back (whole torso) can lengthen and wide

Notice the how the movement of the ribs is positively affected/restored as the body comes into good balance and coordination.

Tension is the number one enemy of free rib movement. Most of us need to learn how let go of unnecessary tension,
STOP INTERFERING, with this movement. Then, it will happen as freely, easily and fully as nature intended.

ⓘ IMPORTANT
On this picture note the location of the ribs in relationship to the pelvis. Many people have mapped the front of their ribs in line with the front of their pelvis. The anatomical reality is quite different. **The front of the ribs is in front of the front of the pelvis**. Ensuring you have this relational mapping correct will positively impact upon the freedom of movement you have in breathing.

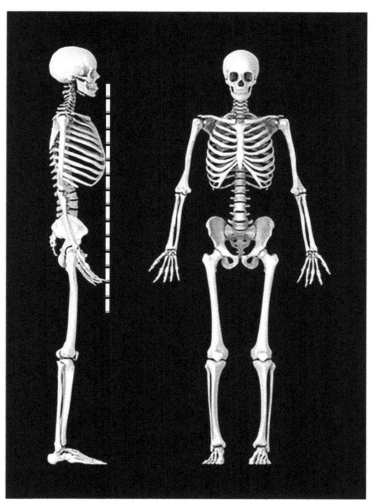

Fig. 23

Part Two

The Organs of Respiration: Lungs

Look back at your drawing from session one. Where and how did your draw your lungs?

❾ DISCUSS and ☙ EXPLORE
Can you indicate where your lungs are located on your own body? How high do they extend? How low? How deep/wide? How would you describe their shape?

On the skeleton, can you show how much of the torso they occupy?

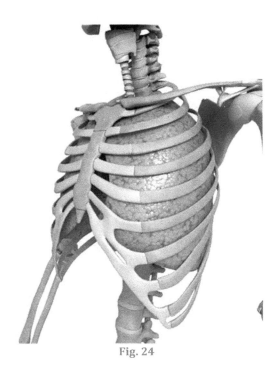

Fig. 24

The Lungs are commonly mapped TOO LOW and are much HIGHER than many people imagine.

The lungs fit within the surrounding structures – the ribs, spine, heart and diaphragm. They extend from above the collarbones to the bottom of the ribs (the 7th rib in front and 10th in back). The lungs are wider at their base and narrower at their apex.

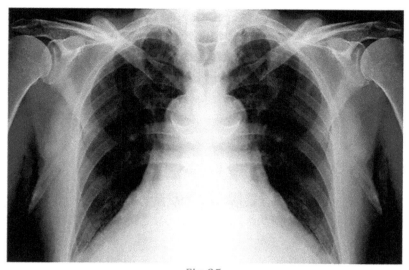
Fig. 25

cs   EXPLORE
With a partner, map the location of the lungs. Remember to include the sides and
top in your mapping.

Part Three

The Muscles of Respiration: Intercostals, Diaphragm, Abdominal Wall and Pelvic Floor

❾ DISCUSS
What muscles of the body are directly involved in breathing?

The primary muscles of breathing are the DIAPHRAM and INTERCOSTALS and the secondary muscles include the ABDOMINALS and PELVIC FLOOR.

Let's begin with the Diaphragm. Go back to your picture from Session One and if you don't have the diaphragm included, draw it in now.

❾ DISCUSS
Point to the location of your diaphragm on your body. Observe where other people are pointing.

Do you think about your diaphragm as moving? If so, can you indicate or describe the direction of this movement?

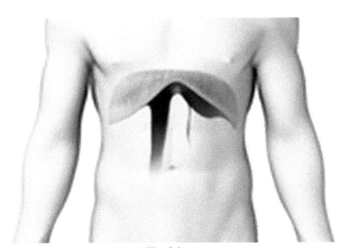

Fig. 26

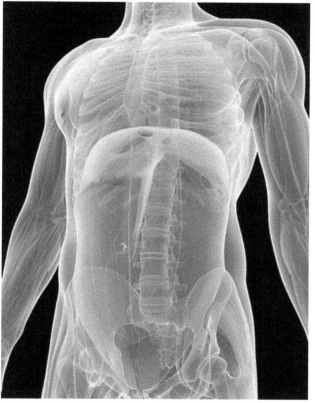

Fig. 27

The Diaphragm is a dome-shaped muscle that rises up inside the ribs and divides the abdominal cavity (lower) from the thoracic cavity (upper) of the torso. It is asymmetrical (slightly lower on the left) to accommodate the heart that is sitting with the lungs above. It is described as having three origins:

✓ Sternal Origin (from the xiphoid process of the sternum)
✓ Costal Origin (from the interior surfaces of ribs 7-12 along the costal arch)
✓ Vertebral Origin (On the right side of front aspect of lumbar spine L1-L3 & on the left side of front aspect of lumbar spine L1-L2)

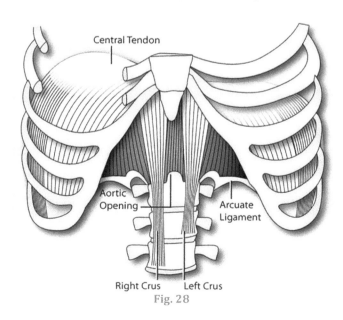

Fig. 28

The diaphragm also has three openings for:

✓ The esophagus (food & liquids)
✓ The inferior vena cava (heart)
✓ The aorta (heart)

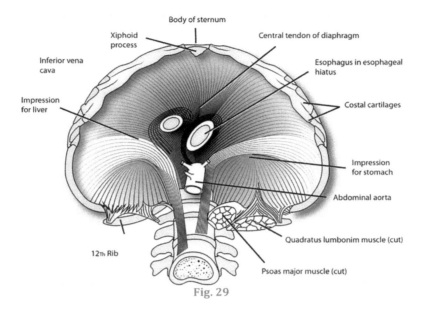

Fig. 29

The dome shape of the diaphragm flattens on Inhalation as the muscle contracts. This contraction exerts a downward pressure on the abdominal cavity and pushes the ribs up and out. On Exhalation the diaphragm resumes its domed shape.

▤ DRAW
In the space below draw the shape and direction of movement (an arrow) the diaphragm makes on INHALATION:

42

▤ DRAW

Now draw the shape and direction of movement (an arrow) the diaphragm makes on EXHALATION:

Rib movement goes hand in hand with good breathing. As just described, when the diaphragm moves it moves the ribs. However, the diaphragm is not the only muscle acting upon the ribs. The External and Internal Intercostal muscles occupy the spaces between adjacent ribs and are arranged atop each other in two thin layers.

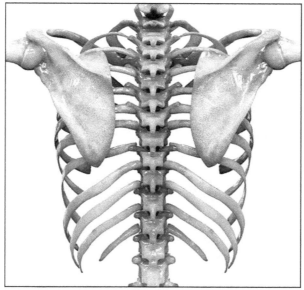

Fig. 30

ⓘ Neither the intercostal muscle fibers nor ribs are horizontal. For this reason we will only create tension if we think of moving our ribs in and out directly sideways when breathing.

When the diaphragm moves downwards, the lower ribs move upward and outward along a curve, expanding the ribcage sideways like bucket handles being lifted.

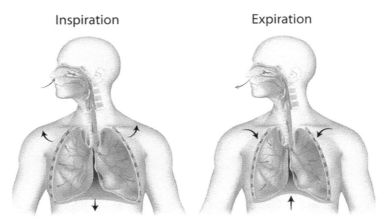

Fig. 31

ଓ EXPLORE
Use your hands to emulate the movement of the ribs, swinging up and out then down and in like 'bucket handles.' Now observe this movement (it will be small) standing in front of the mirror. You may also like to try jumping up and down or running on the spot for a little while in order that your breathing becomes more visible for you to observe its movement.

❾ DISCUSS
What muscles are situated on the front aspect of the torso?
What do we mean when we talk about "Abs"?
Are the "Abs" required in breathing?

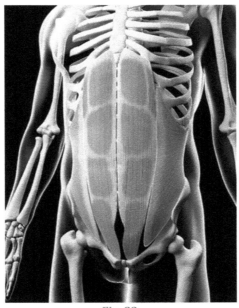

Fig. 32

*As it descends, the diaphragm pushes on the internal abdominal and pelvic contents moving them **outwards against the abdominal wall** in all directions – front, sides and back.*

ભ EXPLORE
Sitting in your chair or standing try this:
'Brace your Abs' and take a large breath in and out.
Now, let go of your 'Braced Abs' and,

☐ RECALL and project the Alexander Directions from Session One:

* Allow the neck to be free *so that*
* the head can go forward and up *so that*
* the back (whole torso) can lengthen and widen

Now, take a deep breath in and out.

❾ DISCUSS
What was the impact of engaging the 'abs' when breathing? Was it helpful or restricting in terms of rib movement, and expansion of the torso in the front, sides and back?

Tension of the abdominal wall will dramatically limit movement of the ribs and the diaphragm = restricted and chaotic breathing!

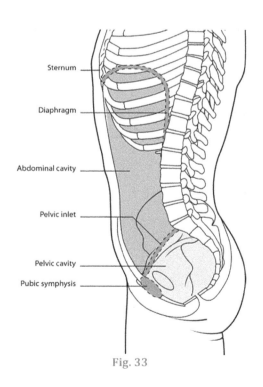

Fig. 33

⊙ DISCUSS
Does the pelvic floor area move? In what direction? How might it be involved in breathing?

▭ RECALL
*As it descends, the diaphragm pushes on the internal abdominal and pelvic contents moving them outwards against the abdominal wall in all directions – front, sides and back **AND downwards against the pelvic floor.***

℞ EXPLORE
With the understanding you have of the pelvic floor muscles, try turning these on (brace, squeeze, tense) and take a deep breath in and out.
Now, let go of your pelvic floor and,

▭ RECALL and project the Alexander Directions from Session One:

- Allow the neck to be free *so that*
- the head can go forward and up *so that*
- the back (whole torso) can lengthen and widen

Now, take a deep breath in and out.

⊙ DISCUSS
What was the impact upon your breathing when you had your pelvic floor turned on? Turned off?

▤ DRAW
Dram a diagram to show the relative position of the diaphragm and pelvic floor both on Exhalation and Inhalation. Using the words Exhale and Inhale, label the diaphragm and pelvic floor.

*Just as tension of the **abdominal wall** will dramatically limit movement of the ribs and the diaphragm so too will tension of the **pelvic floor** = restricted and chaotic breathing!*

❾ DISCUSS
What then is the role of the **abdominal wall** and **pelvic floor** in breathing?

Breathing is a movement that occurs throughout the whole torso in an organized, wave-like manner.

*On Inhalation the intercostal (muscles between ribs) and diaphragm (dome shaped muscle) contract and the whole torso gathers (top to bottom) dragging the diaphragm's central tendon downwards. This descent of the diaphragm **pushes on** the abdominal and pelvic contents and **moves** the pelvic wall out (front, sides and back) and pelvic floor down.*

*On Exhalation the whole torso lengthens slightly, the ribs move down and in and the diaphragm ascends, during which the pelvic floor and abdominal wall **spring back.***

Notice the underlined words in this description of breathing. What qualities do they describe?

Part Four

Mapping our language

The Alexander Technique gives us a process for examining not only what we do, but HOW we do what we do. The abdominal wall and pelvic floor undoubtedly play an important role in breathing. Because they play an important role and because breathing a vital life force(!), it is worth examining HOW you are thinking about, directing and using these muscles.

Read carefully then ▤ HIGHLIGHT the words and definitions below that you believe are the most constructive in relation to directing the way you are using your pelvic floor muscles.

- TENSE (verb): 1. to become or make tense through stretching or straining
- ACTIVATE (verb): 1. to make something capable of action, 2. to mobilize
- HOLD (verb): 1. To fix something in position, 2. To contain something
- BRACE (verb): 1. Prepare for something bad, 2. Assume a position providing support for the body
- WORK (verb): 1. Exert effort or influence, 2. To shape something
- ENGAGE (verb):1. To involve, 2. To require use of something

❾ DISCUSS
What did you choose and why? What words in some of the definitions did you identify and problematic? How does this awareness inform the language you are using to direct yourself?

▤ Give some examples of language that you use that is potentially problematic and what language you could use instead.

SESSION THREE

Part One

The Boney structure of the Upper Arm: Clavicle, Scapula, Humerus and Joints

❾ DISCUSS

What is an arm?
What is a shoulder?

Look back at your drawing from Session One. How did you draw this area and how does it attach to the rest of the body?

☐ RECALL
The arm belongs to the appendicular skeleton.

Anatomically speaking there is no such thing as a shoulder. The term shoulder is much like the term waist. It refers to a general territory not an anatomical location and tends to be understood differently from person to person.

Each arm is made up of a collarbone (clavicle), a scapula, a humerus, radius, ulna, a wrist and a hand. That's a total of 31 bones!

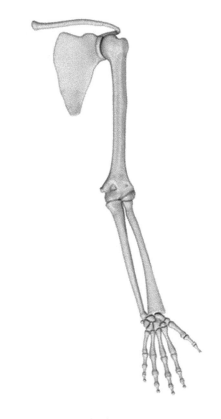

Fig. 34

There are four major joints of the arm:
- ✓ Sternoclavicular Joint
- ✓ Glenohumeral Joint
- ✓ Elbow
- ✓ Wrist

▤ LABEL the 4 joints on the diagram on the previous page, with number 1 being the Sternoclavicular joint.

ന EXPLORE

Stand in front of the mirror and locate by looking and palpating, the sternoclavicular joint. Move your arm around and shrug your shoulders to see it move.

Fig. 35

The only boney attachment of the arm to the rest of the body is at the sternoclavicular joint – where the collarbone (clavicle) meets the sternum.

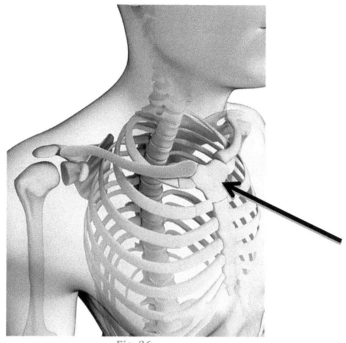

Fig. 36

☐ RECALL

We have just looked at how the arm attaches to the sternum. In this way, the arm is connected to the ribs which are connected to the spine atop which sits the head and at the bottom of which attaches the pelvis to which the legs including feet are attached! This means that the balance of the arm will certainly affect and be affected by the whole body organization.

The collarbones pivot at the sternum and when they move freely they move the entire arm.

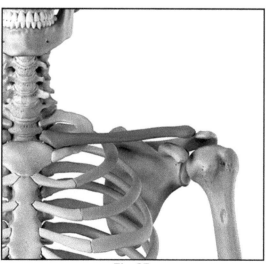

Fig. 37

❾ DISCUSS

Why do we have arms? How is their function different to other parts of our appendicular skeleton i.e. legs? How is the function of the arms evident in the structure? (Arrangement of bones, joint locations and size)

ༀ EXPLORE

Try the following:

Pull your shoulders back and down (traditional idea of "good posture").
The other person can use their hands to palpate the sternoclavicular joint and scapula as you move in and out of this posture.

Now get your partner to observe as you move your arm. Try reaching for something, picking up an object, shrugging maintaining the shoulders pulled back and down.

Swap over roles and repeat.

Discuss with your partner what you noticed, particularly in relation to ease and range of motion at the arm.

Part Two

The Boney structure of the Upper Arm: Scapula

The shoulder blades are attached to the skeleton by muscle. They have no boney attachment to the ribs, spine, skull or each other. For this reason they can move in a variety of ways as pictured here.

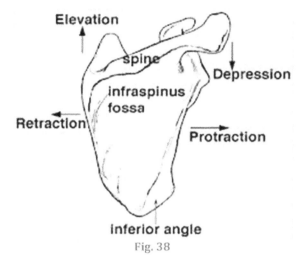
Fig. 38

Ⱕ EXPLORE
Move your scapula together and one at a time in each of the directions illustrated. You can also do this with a partner. The partner can put their hands on your scapula to feel the various movement directions at the same time observing the impact of each movement upon the organization of the whole person.

Fig. 39

The rotation of the shoulder blade over the ribs moves the WHOLE arm structure forward or back at the STERNOCLAVICULAR JOINT.

The scapula and collarbone work in coordination together and moreover, the whole arm organization is dependent upon the balance of this area, front and back and side-to-side!

cs EXPLORE
Here is quick and effective way to restore the balance and suspension of the collar bones and scapula (thus the whole arm):

☐ RECALL and project the Alexander Directions from Session One:

- Allow the neck to be free *so that*
- the head can go forward and up *so that*
- the back (whole torso) can lengthen and widen

Now, sitting or standing perform a number of slow 'shrugging' movements. Actively raise the whole structure on the ascent, then allow the whole structure to descend, being careful not to push or pull down past the point of balance. Most of us will take the descent too far into either pulling the structure back and down or collapsing forward and down.

Using a mirror can be helpful to observe anything 'extra' you are doing. Mostly we are designed such that the collarbones will be horizontal (rather than on a slope) when the arm is in balance.

Fig. 40

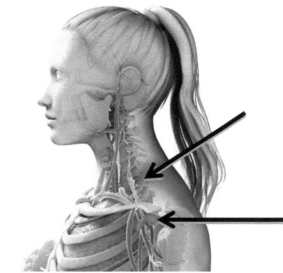
Fig. 41

ⓘ Many nerves, veins and arteries servicing the arm and hand run UNDER the collar bones, between the arm and ribs. If the head, neck, scapula and collarbones are not organized in easy balance, sensation and blood flow can be interrupted causing pain, tingling and numbness throughout the lower arm and hand – a condition often referred to Thoracic Outlet Syndrome.

54

Part Three

The Boney structure of the Upper Arm: Humerus

ᘓ EXPLORE and ❾   DISCUSS

Pass around the scapula, clavicle and HUMERUS bone. Examine how they connect, particularly noting how the humerus connects to the scapula at the glenohumeral joint. Notice the shape and location of this joint socket.

Also have a look on the full skeleton. How is does this joint differ from the leg joint (where the femur attaches to the pelvis)? Why is this and how does it inform function?

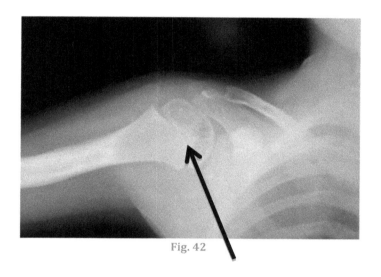

Fig. 42

How would you point to your glenohumeral joint?

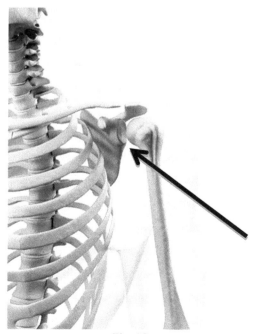

Fig. 43

ଔ EXPLORE

Standing, raise your arm in front of you as far as it will go. Now try the reverse, raising the arm behind you as far as it will go. Which way has the greatest range of movement?

Now, raise your arm in front of you, this time stopping as soon as you notice you are moving at more than just the glenohumeral joint. How far can you move before other parts of the arm (clavicle and scapula) become involved? Are you surprised by this?

Fig. 44

Fig. 45

Fig. 46

The arms are happiest moving in front of us due to the location of the structure and their function – to perform lifting, pushing, catching tasks in front of us where the eyes can see!

Fig. 47

Fig. 48

ⓘYou may have heard physiotherapists use the term humero-scapular rhythm. What are they referring to and why is it important?

Humero-scapular rhythm is a fancy name for the relational functioning of the humerus bone and scapular in movement i.e. Picking up a book.

Many people don't allow the scapular to move sufficiently, they may even brace this area while moving the humerus bone. This can cause pain and restricted range of motion. Proper humero-scapular rhythm can be restored by sending your Alexander technique directions and then including the collar bone and scapula in your conception of arm movement and allow the arm to move at all its joints.

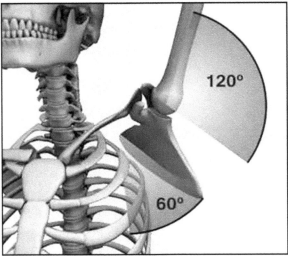
Fig. 49

ↈ EXPLORE
Before going on to look at the lower arm, wrist and hand, why not try some activities using the arms.

RECALL
How you have mapped your body DIRECTLY informs how you move. In this way, moving will give you accurate feedback on how you are now thinking about, thus mapping your body. In this case, the arms.

Some good activities to do in relation to arm movement are:

- ✓ Playing a ball game
- ✓ Picking up objects
- ✓ Typing on a keyboard
- ✓ Playing the piano or another instrument that uses the whole arm
- ✓ Opening and closing doors or cupboards
- ✓ Writing on a white/chalk board

⬚ RECALL and project the Alexander Directions to whatever activity you choose:

- Allow the neck to be free *so that*
- the head can go forward and up *so that*
- the back (whole torso) can lengthen and widen

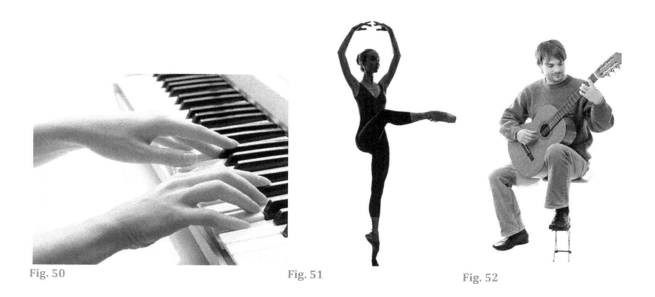

Fig. 50   Fig. 51   Fig. 52

Notes

SESSION FOUR

Part One

Elbow and Forearm bones

☐ RECALL

What does the arm consist of?
Why is "shoulder" not such a useful term?
How many major joints does the arm have?
Point to and move joints 1 and 2 which we covered in Session Three.

❾ DISCUSS
The third joint of the arm is the elbow. How many bones make up the elbow joint?
Is hinge a good description of the movement that occurs at this joint?

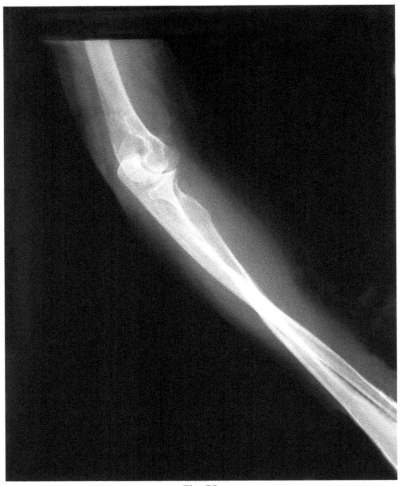

Fig. 53

At the elbow we make TWO different types of movement. Bending AND rotation. Many of us are not familiar with the rotational possibilities at this joint.

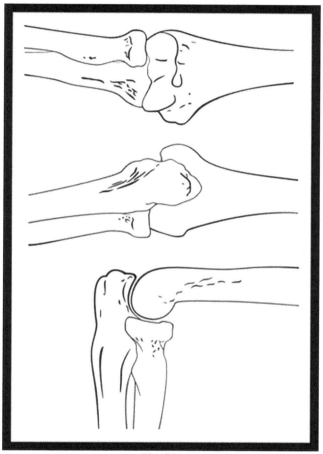

Fig. 54

ॐ EXPLORE
Sitting or standing in front of a mirror, bend your elbow so that you can touch your fingers to your shoulder. Try to do this movement just using the elbow joint. Then, with your arms hanging long by your sides, face the palms toward the mirror. Now, rotate your arm inward at the elbow joint so that the palm moves to face behind you.

❾ DISCUSS
Looking back at the picture of the elbow and from the two movement possibilities you have just explored, it is evident that the relationship of the three arm bones at the elbow is rather interesting… ingenious even!

Bend your elbow and palpate it. Locate your 'funny bone' (the boney prominence that hurts if you knock it!). What arm bone does it belongs to? Is it the humerus, or one of the forearm bones? Quite aptly, the 'funny bone' belongs to the humerus. We will come back to this a little bit later.

Supination   Pronation

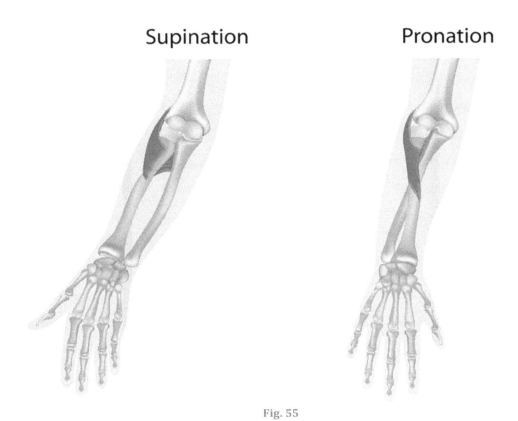

Fig. 55

▤ Label (and colour if it helps!) the two pictures of the forearm, 1. Palm facing down (pronation) 2. Palm facing up (supination)

The Radius (thumb side) rotates around the Ulna (little finger side as axis.

Palm Up, the Radius and Ulna are parallel.
Palm Down, the Radius and Ulna are crossed.

▢ RECALL and cs EXPLORE
Earlier we established that the 'funny bone' at the elbow belongs to the humerus. Palpate the funny bone again. Now rotate the lower arm (from the elbow down to the finger) keeping contact with your 'funny bone'. Notice that the 'funny bone' thus humerus does not move and therefore is NOT involved in this rotation movement.

Get an A4 sheet of paper and a pen or pencil.

Set yourself up seated at a table, ensuring the table is not too high for you and your forearms can comfortably rest on it.

Place one arm *palm side up* (supine) on the sheet of paper and trace an outline of your lower arm, wrist and hand. Now, face the palm down (pronate) and again, trace around the lower arm, wrist and hand.

Label each outline accordingly – supination and pronation.

Now draw and label the Ulna and Radius on each. ☐ RECALL that the relationship between these bones changes from palm up (supination) to palm down (pronation). Now, on your two outlines draw a line from tip of the thumb, all the way along the radius to where the elbow would be.

From this drawing, it will become clear to you that:

❾ DISCUSS
What might be the implications of knowing and thus rotating (pronating and supinating) from the elbow? How might a person perform these movements without this mapping? In what activities might this be important?

ɔɜ EXPLORE
At this point, you may wish to further explore the radius as axis in an activity such as typing or playing the piano.

Fig. 56

63

This first picture illustrates the line of integrity through the lower arm and how in this person this line of integrity is being interrupted with sideways flexion at the wrist known as Ulna deviation.

Try this for yourself and observe how it feels. As you can probably observe, it increases strain in the hand, wrist and lower arm and if sustained i.e. in long periods of typing, can lead to RSI (repetitive strain injury).

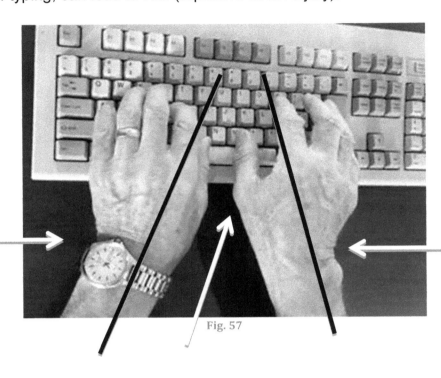

Fig. 57

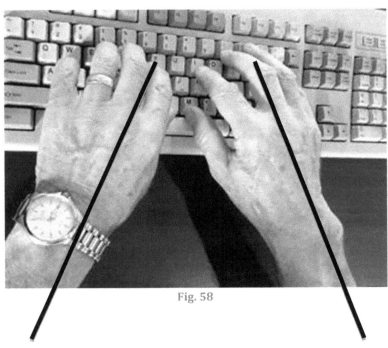

Fig. 58

The most efficient and restful relationship of the hand and forearm is the little finger in line with the ulna. This means the thumb DOES NOT line up with the radius.

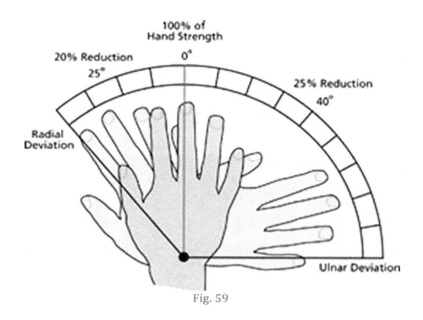

Fig. 59

Part Two

The Wrist

☐ **RECALL**
Look back at your numbered diagram of the arm, now noting joint number 4 - the wrist.

❾ **DISCUSS**
What constitutes a wrist? How did you draw this area in your picture way back in Session One? How would you describe the movement that happens at this joint? Having thought about this description, does this inform how you might draw the wrist?

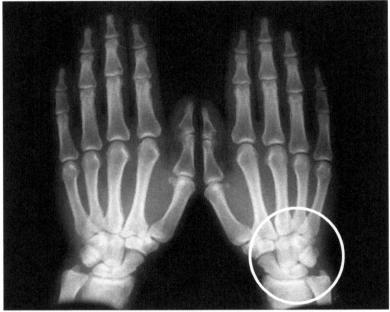

Fig. 60

The wrist comprises a cluster of 8 small bones. This enables many more movement possibilities and subtle articulations than what is commonly mapped - a straight hinge joint between the forearm bones and hand.

▤ **Draw**
Go back now to your earlier 'arm tracing' picture, and draw in the 8 wrist bones. Refer to the picture above as needed.

☙ EXPLORE

Sitting or standing, palpate arm joints 1, 2, 3 and 4 – the wrist. Staying at the wrist, LOOK at it as you explore its movement possibilities. As you SEE your wrist, consider the three-dimensionality of this area comprised of 8 small bones. Swap sides and repeat the exploration.

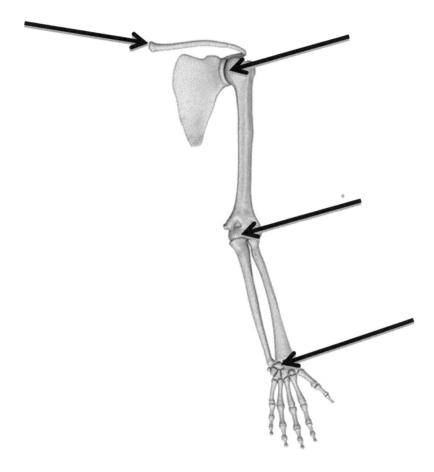

Fig. 61

ⓘ Carpal tunnel syndrome is a painful disorder of the hand caused by pressure on nerves that run through the wrist. Symptoms include numbness, pins and needles, and pain (particularly at night). Anything that causes swelling inside the wrist can cause carpal tunnel syndrome, including repetitive hand movements, pregnancy and arthritis. Possible treatments include rest, splinting, cortisone injections and surgery. Alexander technique is very effective in relieving carpal tunnel problems via restoration of the Primary control and attention to the use of the hands and wrists in activity.

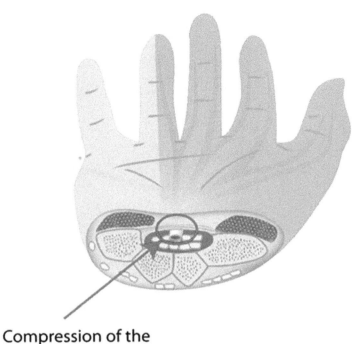

Compression of the median nerve

Fig. 62

Part Three

The Hand

❾ DISCUSS

What is a hand? How many bones make up a hand?
Why do we have a thumb?
How is the hand similar and different to the foot? Why might this be?

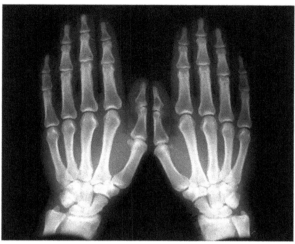

Fig. 63

Looking at this picture we can see that each finger comprises 4 bones and the thumb has just 3 bones.

ଓ EXPLORE

Look at and palpate your own hands. Palpate, move and count each of the four finger bones and 3 thumb bones. Turn your hand palm side up and look at the crease lines in your skin, especially where the finger meets the palm of the hand. Now try to bend at this crease line. NOT POSSIBLE (!) Curiously, if you once again palpate the bones of the fingers you will start to notice that the flesh encasing doesn't correspond directly with the underlying boney structure.

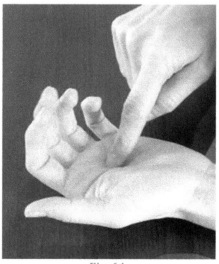

Fig. 64

▤ Draw
With the information you are gathering about your fingers and thumb, go back to your 'arm tracing' and draw in these bones. Be as accurate as you can in terms of how the outline (skin, flesh) corresponds with the bones.

❾ DISCUSS
Let's come back to the question of, why do we have a thumb?
What would happen if we didn't have a thumb?

୰ EXPLORE
On your own hand, palpate the first joint of the thumb. Notice how this joint is right back near the wrist. Now move your thumb including all its joints to touch the tip of each finger one at a time. Once you have done this, try the same movement but this time stopping the thumb from moving at the first joint. Do you notice how it is more difficult to bring the thumb across to touch each fingertip?

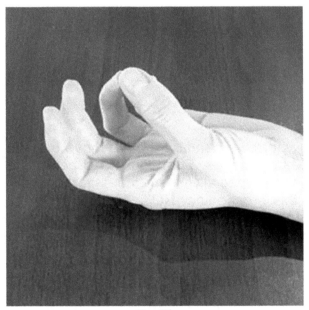

Fig. 65

If you have mapped the thumb with only two joints and move as such, you may suffer restricted movement and visible over prominence of the second thumb joint. If you use your WHOLE thumb, including all three joints, you will experience greater mobility and strength especially in grasping and holding movements.

70

Part Four

Putting it all together: The Whole Arm

▤ Draw

Get yourself a large piece of butchers paper and a felt pen. Without overthinking, and using your whole arm including all 4 joints, draw your left and right arm.

ଔ EXPLORE

With all the information you have gathered about your arms, you could use any of the following activities to continue the process of exploration and integration:

- ✓ Ball games – juggling, in a circle with a group
- ✓ Picking up objects
- ✓ Typing, text messaging
- ✓ Playing a musical instrument – piano, guitar, flute, clarinet etc.
- ✓ Domestic chores – washing up, chopping
- ✓ Exercises – push-ups, lifting weights
- ✓ Personal care – brushing teeth, washing and brushing hair, applying make-up

Whichever activities you choose, ▭ RECALL and project the Alexander directions:

- • Allow the neck to be free *so that*
- • the head can go forward and up *so that*
- • the back (whole torso) can lengthen and widen

…so that you can do you can use your whole arm to do the chosen activity.

Fig. 66   Fig. 67   Fig. 68

SESSION FIVE

Part One

Overview of the Leg

⬚ RECALL and ▤ Draw
Look back at your drawing of the spine from Session One.
Re-draw your spine in the space provided. Then, add your pelvis, legs and feet.

❾ DISCUSS
Why do we have a pelvis and legs? Why might it be important to know that your legs connect into the axial skeleton via the pelvis?
How many bones make up each leg?
How many major joints?

▤ Label
Mark each of the three major joint areas of the leg in this picture: the hip, knee and ankle joints.

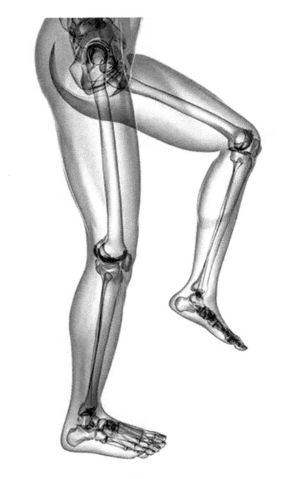

Fig. 69

Part Two

The Pelvis

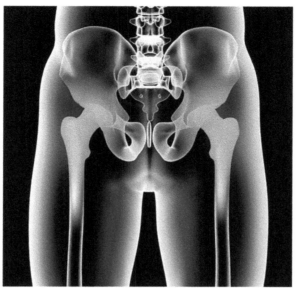

Fig. 70

In standing the Pelvis receives the weight of the upper body and transfers it to the legs. Conversely it absorbs the upward thrust of the legs generated in walking, running, jumping.

In sitting the pelvis receives the weight of the upper body and transfers it to the... chair!

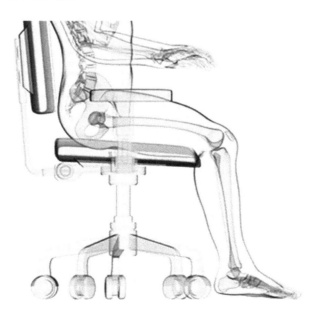

Fig. 71

▤ Draw

On this chair and using the picture you have just labeled to help, draw a person in sitting. Pay particular attention to how you draw the spine, pelvis and legs relative to each other in sitting.

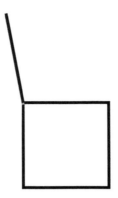

❾ DISCUSS

What part/s of the body have you drawn making contact with the chair? What are we sitting on when we sit in balance?

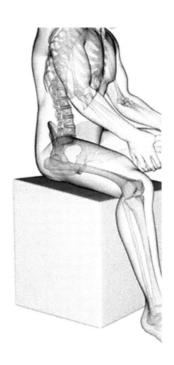

Fig. 72

We don't sit on our leg bones. We sit on a part of our pelvis known as the ischial tuberosities or sitz bones.

cଃ EXPLORE
Palpate your sitz bones while sitting on a chair and also in standing.
Sitting in a chair, ☐   RECALL and project the Alexander directions:

* Allow the neck to be free *so that*
* the head can go forward and up *so that*
* the back (whole torso) can lengthen and widen

so that you can …explore rocking forwards and backwards on your sitz bones.

Notice in your rocking that there is a place where the balance seems easiest or most efficient.

Also while you are exploring rocking on your sitz bones, try collapsing in your seat and conversely doing 'good posture' or pulling up. Again, notice the effect, at the pelvis and through the whole body.

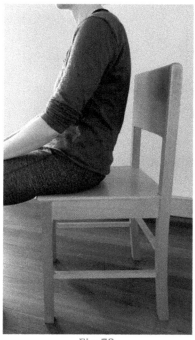

Fig. 73

Fig. 74

❾   DISCUSS
What did you observe at the pelvis and in your whole self when you rocked off balance sitting backwards and also forwards? How might the balance of the head on the spine impact the pelvis and vice versa?

▱ If we sit rocked too far forward, weight goes through the pubic symphysis at the front of the pelvis. If we sit rocked too far back, weight goes through the coccyx (last part of spine). In both cases weight is traveling through a part of the body not intended to take weight and for this reason can cause pain and injury if done constantly over a period of time.

Part Three

Hip Joint and Upper Leg

❾ DISCUSS and ଌ EXPLORE
What are we referring to when we say hip? What about hip joint?
Stand up where you are. Now point to your hip joint. Take a look around the group. Are there variations on where people are pointing?

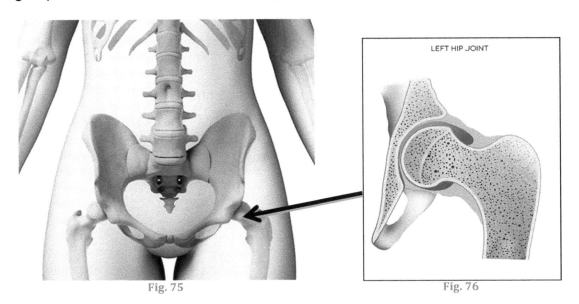

| Fig. 75 | Fig. 76 |

ⓘ 'Hip' tends not to be a useful term. Like 'shoulder' and 'waist,' the term 'hip' refers to a general area rather than specific, anatomical reality. Hip joint is a much more useful term to use when referring to the meeting of the leg bone (femur) and pelvis at the iliofemoral joint.

🗐 Label the following on this diagram:

      ✓ Hip joints (iliofemeral joint)
      ✓ Sitz bones (ischial tuberosities)
      ✓ Leg bones (femur)

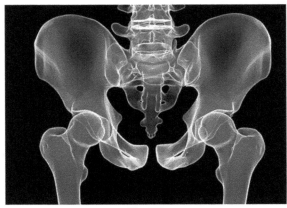

Fig. 77

Stand up and with the information you are gathering, use your index fingers to point to your hip joints. Keeping your fingers there, try some small squatting movements and some marching on the spot.

Fig. 78

❾   DISCUSS and cx   EXPLORE

What might be the consequence of not bending accurately at the hip joint? Try bending from a location much higher than the joint, the iliac crest (top part of pelvis) as you pick something up off the floor. This is a common mis-mapping of the hip joint and as you will experience, it is the spine that actually does the bending since it's the only joint at this location.

Fig. 79

Fig. 80

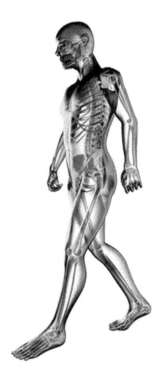

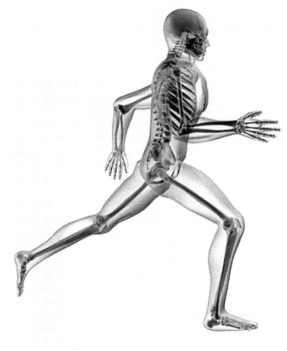

Fig. 82

Fig. 81

The angle and structure of the thigh bones (femurs) as well as their connection to the external aspect of the pelvis is a superb arrangement. It is what allows the legs to move freely and clear the pelvis when we sit, walk and run!

cs EXPLORE

With the information you have just gathered about the relationship between the leg bones and pelvis try the following activity -

⬚   RECALL and project the Alexander directions:

• Allow the neck to be free *so that*
• the head can go forward and up *so that*
• the back (whole torso) can lengthen and widen

Now leading with your head, rock forward on your sitz bones, to pick up something on the floor, remaining in contact with the chair. Once you have the item in your hand, pause, give your Alexander directions and reverse the movement to return back to balanced sitting.

ⓘ When sitting on the floor with legs stretched out in front, most adults will be unable to sit on their ischial tuberosities or sitz bones. This is usually due to tight hamstrings and causes the person to slump. A person with long hamstrings will be able to sit right up on their sitz bones and have the spine in healthy length. Note! A long spine in sitting still has its curves as pictured in the second diagram Fig 5.16.

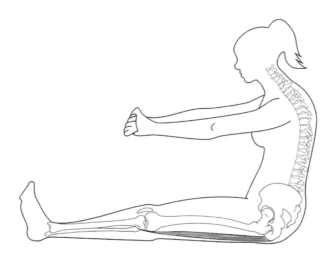

Fig. 83

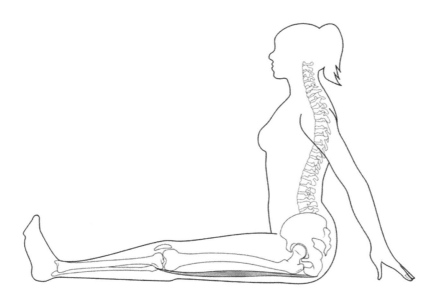

Fig. 84

You may also like to explore your new understanding of the relationship between the leg and pelvis in:

- ✓ squatting (alone, with a chair or partner, see picture below)
- ✓ getting in and out of a chair
- ✓ walking and running on flat surface and up stairs
- ✓ riding a bike
- ✓ freestyle or backstroke swimming
- ✓ bending to pick something up
- ✓ getting in and out of the car

Fig. 85

Fig. 86

☐ RECALL and ▤ Label

On this, use dotted lines and arrows to indicate the delivery of weight through the pelvis

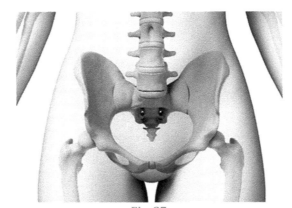

Fig. 87

Part Four

The Knee

❾ DISCUSS
Take a look back at your drawing of your body from Session One. Did you include knees? If so, how did you draw them?
What is a knee? What is a knee cap?
Why do we have knees? How would movement be different without them?

☙ EXPLORE
Stand up and point to your knee joint. Take a look around and notice if there is variation in where people are pointing.
You can accurately point to the three-dimensional knee joint from the sides, back and just under (standing)/below (sitting) the patella in front.

The knee joint is commonly mapped too high as if the joint is located at the readily palpable patella (knee cap). The knee joint is in fact much lower. It is the meeting of the thigh bone (femur) and lower leg bone (tibia).

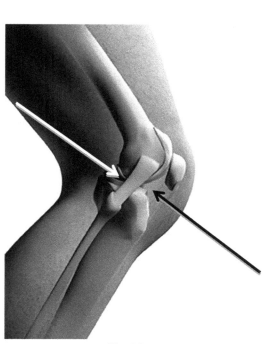

Fig. 88

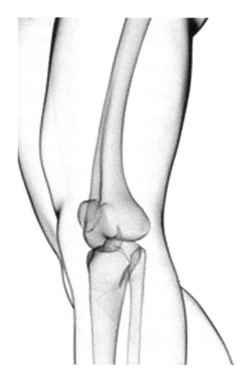

Fig. 89

81

Stand and explore the 3 possible states of the knee, observing which feels most habitual or familiar to you:

- LOCKED
- BENT
- BALANCED (NEUTRAL)

Fig. 90

Knee locking actually functions to stop us from falling backwards when the pelvis is pushed forward (which causes the head to move backward off balance). In this way knee balance can be positively influenced by addressing the balance of the whole body. When we stop pushing the pelvis forward, re-balance the head atop the spine there is no longer any need to lock the knees.

cx EXPLORE

With a partner and using the mirror take it in turns to stand with LOCKED, BENT and BALANCED knees. Observe how this looks and feels and the influence each state has on the whole body balance.

Secondly, stand as you normally would then purposely pull your head back and down off balance. What do you do to keep balanced? Where do you do this?
Now, ☐ RECALL and project the Alexander directions:

- Allow the neck to be free *so that*
- the head can go forward and up *so that*
- the back (whole torso) can lengthen and widen

How does rebalancing your head on top of your spine affect your whole balance? What do you no longer have to do to stay on balance?

① You may have heard physiotherapists, personal trainers, dance teachers and the like say, "knees over toes" in bending movement. What exactly do they mean and why might this be an important instruction?

The knee is not inherently stable or fitted together like the elbow. It relies on ligaments (cruciate and collateral) to provide stability and prevent rotation at what is essentially a hinge joint. The knee joint is also cushioned with a meniscus (cartilaginous disc) that sits between the femur and tibia.

If the knees are not tracking accurately over the feet (twisting), the patella does not track smoothly through the femoral groove, the stabilizing ligaments get pulled and the meniscus receives an uneven distribution of weight. Both acute and chronic knee injury can result from mal-alignment combined with bearing weight.

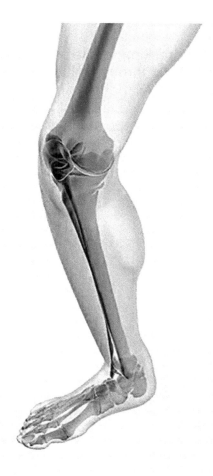

Fig. 91

Earlier we examined the angle of the femur bones in relation to the pelvis. This angle also informs the movement direction of the knees in bending. Alexander instructed using the words, *knees forward and away* to direct the knees over the feet, especially in sitting, standing and walking movements.

You can add this secondary direction to the primary directions:
- Allow the neck to be free *so that*
- the head can go forward and up *so that*
- the back (whole torso) can lengthen and widen *so that*
- the knees can move forward and away

It may be useful to imagine the knees as having two headlights and are bending along parallel train tracks that will never intersect.

గ్ర EXPLORE
With a partner explore the tracking of the legs in the movement of sitting and standing. One person can move through sitting and standing, while the other can kneel or sit in front and use their hand to gently direct the knees forward and away. Swap roles and when you are finished, discuss with your partner what you noticed. Was it difficult, easy, different and in what ways?

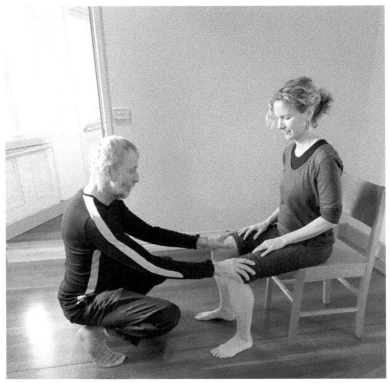

Fig. 92

SESSION SIX

Part One

Lower Leg and Ankle

☐ RECALL and ❾ DISCUSS
How many major joints make up each leg? What is the third joint?
Looking back at your drawing from Session One, how did you draw your ankle?
What might be wrong about the ankle in the stick figure below?

Fig. 93

▤ Circle which of these diagrams best represents the anatomical reality of the ankle joint.

❾ DISCUSS your choice and why you have made this choice.

Palpate and point to your ankle joint. Observe where others are pointing. Is there variation?

The ankle joint comprises the distal ends of the two lower leg bones (tibia and fibula) and the talus bone of the foot.

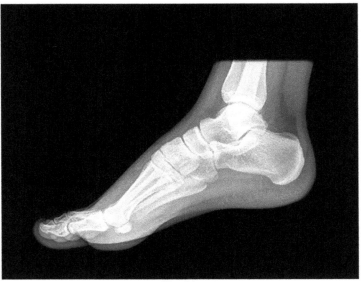
Fig. 94

From this picture of the ankle (without the muscles and tendons) it is apparent that the upside down T is a more accurate diagrammatic representation of the anatomical reality of this joint.

We can also see that when we palpate the boney prominences (malleoli) on the inside (medial) and outside (lateral) aspects of the ankle area, we are reasonably close to the actual ankle joint location.

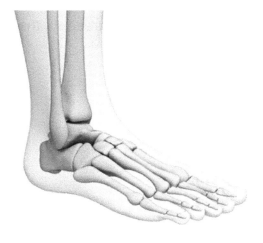
Fig. 95

Because of the tight fit of the bones at the ankle joint, it is only capable of pure flexion (plantar flexion) and extension (dorsiflexion) movements. Anything else involves articulations between the bones of the feet, and is thus not considered true ankle joint movement.

❧ EXPLORE

ⓘ This exploration requires care and needs to be thoroughly understood prior to commencement.

Find yourself a partner and a clear piece of wall to stand in front of.
One person stands half to one whole foot length away from and facing the wall with eyes closed. The partner stands directly behind, facing in the same direction. Both individuals ☐ RECALL and project the Alexander directions:

- Allow the neck to be free *so that*
- the head can go forward and up *so that*
- the back (whole torso) can lengthen and widen

The person with eyes closed begins the exploration. Place the hands on the wall in front and leading with the head (keeping the whole body connected i.e. don't push with the chest, hips or knees) lean forward from the ankle joints and take the weight in the hands. You will notice that the ankle joint flexes (dorsiflexion) and the weight is more forward in the front of your feet. Come back to upright and repeat as many times as you wish, each time very consciously thinking about the motion at the ankle joint.
This motion can then be reversed with the assistance of the partner standing behind. The partner places both hands somewhere near the scapular of the back and both individuals

☐ RECALL and project the Alexander directions:

- Allow the neck to be free *so that*
- the head can go forward and up *so that*
- the back (whole torso) can lengthen and widen

The person with eyes closed moves backwards (keeping the whole body connected) with the support of the partner, such that the ankle joint extends (plantar flexion) and the weight is off center. The partner can then use their hands to move the person with eyes closed back to standing on their own feet. Repeat as many times as you wish, each time very consciously thinking about the motion at the ankle joint.

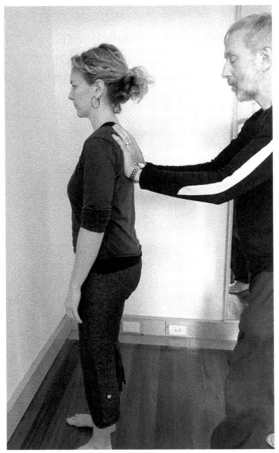

Fig. 96

❾ DISCUSS

What did you discover in the experiment with your partner? Why might freedom and balance at the ankle joints be important to balanced upright standing, particularly in relation to weight distribution through the foot to the ground?

ભ EXPLORE

Peddling is another way to explore ankle joint movement. ☐ RECALL and palpate the area of your ankle joint, remembering that for many people it is lower, more forward and deeper than previously mapped.

☐ RECALL and project the Alexander directions so that you can lift the ball of the foot onto the peddle surface or edge. Experiment with the peddling motion here, consciously thinking about the plantar and dorsiflexion at the ankle joint and the heel acting as a leaver at the other end of the ball of the foot.

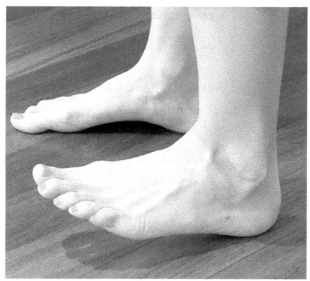
Fig. 97

This exploration is applicable and important to anyone who:

✓ plays piano or organ
✓ plays a drum kit
✓ musicians and conductors who 'tap' their foot to keep time
✓ uses a hydraulic lift chair for patients (i.e. dentist)
✓ drives a car or truck
✓ works in a factory
✓ uses a sewing machine

Part Two

The Foot

The foot is at once a foundation – a firm and stable base of support – and a flexible, adaptable lever that can maneuver us through irregular terrain.[11]

❾ DISCUSS and ✄ EXPLORE
Look back at your drawing from Session One. How did you draw your feet? How did you draw your hands? Does one have more detail than the other?
Did you draw a shoe even?
Why do we have feet? How are they structurally similar and different to the hands?
Examine the foot on the skeleton or strung together from box of bones.

Each foot contains 26 bones, 33 joints and more than 100 muscles that work together to provide support, balance and mobility.

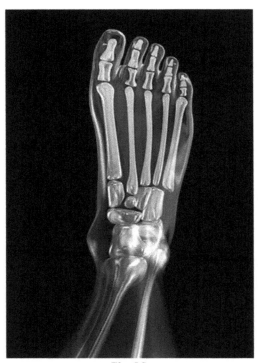
Fig. 98

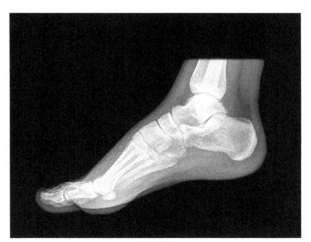
Fig. 99

---

[11] Franklin, Eric. *Dynamic Alignment Through Imagery*, Champaign USA, Human Kinetics, 1996, p. 186.

▤ DRAW

Take two pieces of A4 paper and a pen. Remove your shoes and socks; place the sole of your foot on the paper and trace around it. Repeat so that you have an outline of both feet.

Using the pictures of the feet here provided, in particular the 'above view', roughly draw the bones of the feet onto ONE of you feet tracings.

☐ RECALL what we discovered in Session Four, Part Three – Hand. The flesh including creases and webbing between fingers does not necessarily correspond with the underlying boney structure.

ଔ EXPLORE

You can explore the ongoing, 'micro-movements' at the ankle and foot by doing what modern dance pioneer Steve Paxton[12] termed, a Small Dance. Stand with your feet approximately a fist width apart.

☐ RECALL and project the Alexander directions:

- Allow the neck to be free *so that*
- the head can go forward and up *so that*
- the back (whole torso) can lengthen and widen

Close your eyes and just stand for a few moments. Begin by observing the subtle yet noticeable movements happening through your whole body even though you are relatively 'still'. Now, bring your attention to your ankles and feet. See if you can detect the amount of movement going on in this area in order for you to stand up. Finally, you may like to exaggerate this by leading with your head and connecting through your whole body to shift your weight forwards, backwards (slightly) and side to side. You are now doing a Small Dance!

Fig. 100

_____

[12] http://en.wikipedia.org/wiki/Steve_Paxton

When we walk there is a sequence of movement and weight shift through the foot. Without footwear*, the center of the heel strikes the ground first, the weight is then transferred in quick succession through the lateral border (outside edge) and into the ball of the foot. The heel responds to the weight in the ball of the foot by lifting and the big toe performs a final 'push off' propelling us into the next step.

*(With footwear this sequence of movement is modified (subtly or grossly depending upon the shoe design and fit), and can often be evidenced by examining how the tread of the shoe is worn down.)

... the toes and reflexes act as very efficient and effortless means of propulsion. The foot can sustain enormous amounts of pressure while remaining so flexible that we often refer to people as having a spring in their step when they walk.[13]

❾ DISCUSS

How many arches does the foot have? How might these be an important factor in relation to the springy and resilient qualities associated with a healthy foot?

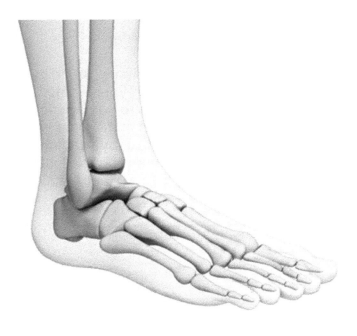

Fig. 101

Each foot has three arches through which the incoming weight of your body is distributed.

Transverse – from the first to the fifth metatarsal heads near junction with the toes
Medial Longitudinal – from the heel to the head of the first metatarsal
Lateral Longitudinal – from the heel to the head of the fifth metatarsal

---

[13] Brennan, Richard. *Change Your Posture, Change Your Life: How the power of the Alexander Technique can combat back pain, tension and stress*, London, Watkins Publishing, 2012, p.139.

▤ DRAW

Label these three arches on the foot pictured above.

* The terms transverse, medial and lateral pertain to the anatomical planes of the body

Note that the toes are not part of the arches and in this way we don't need to grip them *if we are standing in balance and therefore the weight can be received through the arches.*

The arches of the foot, which are built into its bony structure, are supported by both ligaments and muscles… so the arches of the foot are actively supported by muscles and in this sense are part of the postural system, which explains why <u>*the condition of the feet and arches is dependent on the overall working of the postural muscles that support the skeleton.*</u>[14]

ⓘ The picture you have labeled pertains to static upright standing, which is only one of thousands of ways we may be on our feet during the course of a day! It is good to remember that *the foot with all its bones, joints and muscles is highly movable, adaptable and ever changing in response to shifts of weight from above and changes in terrain below.*

<u>*Mobility*</u> *in our feet is important as it allows proper weight distribution through all three arches. Collapsed or fallen arches are regularly caused by ongoing, improper weight distribution through the feet.*[15]

ೞ EXPLORE

Standing or sitting, place a small ball (tennis or acupressure) under your foot and roll the foot over it. You can experiment with putting a little or a lot of weight through the foot. Swap feet. During your exploration, do some areas of the foot seem more tense or tender? You can wonder about this in relation to how you stand and how your feet may be receiving the weight of your whole body.

The toes (in particular the big toes), <u>*propel*</u> *us into each new step.*

---

[14] Dimon, Theodore Jr. *Anatomy of the Moving Body: A Basic Course in Bones, Muscles and Joints*, California, North Atlantic Books, 2008, p.244.

[15] Refer to this article for more information on the relationship between collapsed arches and toe alignment https://nwfootankle.com/files/TestimonialCorrectToes.pdf

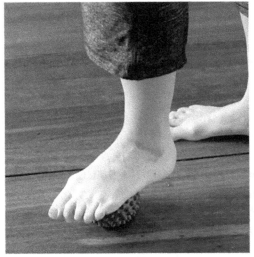
Fig. 102

Fig. 103

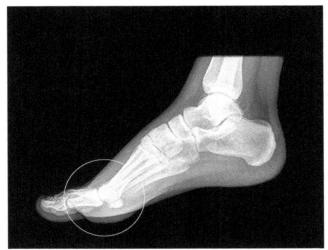
Fig. 104

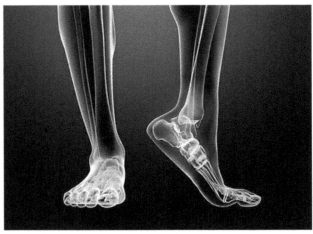
Fig. 105

ભ EXPLORE

Stand comfortably with the feet about a fist width apart.

☐   RECALL and project the Alexander directions:

- Allow the neck to be free *so that*
- the head can go forward and up *so that*
- the back (whole torso) can lengthen and widen

Now, rise up 'like a dancer' onto the balls of your feet. Pause briefly then lower the heels to bring you back to standing. Repeat a couple of times.

❾   DISCUSS

What movements happened at the feet in this exploration? Point to where the foot bends at the big toe (metatarsophalangeal) joint.

▤   Draw a picture of your foot as it would appear in Part 4 of the walking sequence:

Part 1 - *foot strikes the ground, heel first then rolls forward*
Part 2 - *foot flat on floor with full weight spread throughout*
Part 3 – *weight moves into front of foot, toes spread apart slightly*
Part 4 - *heel leaves ground, propulsion through toes*
Part 5 – *toes leave the ground (big toe last)*

Part Three

Putting it all together: Footwear, Standing and Walking

❾ DISCUSS
How might footwear interfere with natural movement of the foot? What kinds of footwear do you consider would be most problematic and why?

… all shoes automatically convert the normal to the abnormal, the natural to the unnatural. (Podiatrist Dr William Rossi, 'Why Shoes Make Normal Gait Impossible') [16]

The reality is that mostly we wear shoes. In this way, it is important to develop an awareness of how you are moving in your chosen footwear and explore if this is the most efficient, easeful use of your whole self in response to the circumstances present? Mostly, we neglect to adapt to our ever-changing circumstances. Take for example a woman who alternates between wearing flat shoes and high heels. If she neglects to consciously consider and adopt a new balance of herself required when she wears her heels (the body moves 20 degrees forward off balance in a 5cm heel), she will most likely tighten some part/s of her body in order to stop herself falling forward. She will do well to spend some time in her heels consciously mapping her joints and their movement range in this modified scenario. For example, the ankle joint is constantly in plantar flexion, so it's reasonable to expect the knee and hip joints will have to move more to make up for the limited ankle joint movement.

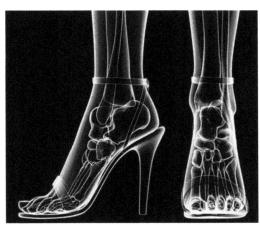

Fig. 106

Fig. 107

---

[16] Podiatrist Dr William Rossi cited in Brennan, Richard. *Change Your Posture, Change Your Life: How the power of the Alexander Technique can combat back pain, tension and stress*, London, Watkins Publishing, 2012, p.139.

❾   DISCUSS and ☙   EXPLORE

What are some common foot dysfunctions you have seen or experienced? How might these be negatively or positively impacted by a person's overall coordination?
What characterizes a healthy foot?
What are we looking for in a good pair of shoes?

↵ LATER
In the appendix of this manual you will find a series of foot exercises that your trainer may take you through.

❾   DISCUSS and ☙   EXPLORE
What is standing? Is there a 'right' and 'wrong' way to stand?
How might our standing be informed by the information we have gathered so far in our Body Mapping?

It is important to recognize that standing is an activity rather than a position. If you watch a young child standing, you will see that they are not actually still, but swaying very gently in balance.[17]

---

[17] Brennan, Richard. *Change Your Posture, Change Your Life: How the power of the Alexander Technique can combat back pain, tension and stress*, London, Watkins Publishing, 2012, p. 121.

Integration Moment

ଔ EXPLORE

With a partner or in a large group (make a circle), take turns to stand.

☐ RECALL and project the Alexander directions:

- Allow the neck to be free *so that*
- the head can go forward and up *so that*
- the back (whole torso) can lengthen and widen

☐ RECALL

So far we have explored balanced functioning of your skeletal structure in the following areas:

- ✓ The balance of your head on your spine at the AO joint
- ✓ The curves of the whole spine through its 24 individual vertebra
- ✓ The highly moveable, 24 individual ribs joining at the back with the spine and in front with the sternum
- ✓ The whole arm with its 4 major joints starting with the sternoclavicular joint
- ✓ The pelvis through which weight is transferred into the legs in standing or the sitz bones (ischial tuberosities) in sitting
- ✓ The leg bones and the joints of the knees, ankles and feet that receive the incoming weight of the rest of the body and take the body into locomotion

Take a moment now as you stand to scan through and review these areas.
As you continue to stand, begin to speak out loud some of the following:

- ✓ Observations - how you feel, what you can see and hear as you stand on the spot
- ✓ Directions - thoughts or instructions you are giving yourself as you stand
- ✓ Wonderings - anything you are wondering about

Swap over with your partner or if in a large group continue around the circle.

▤ Draw

Without too much deliberation, draw a picture of yourself to depict your standing. Find ways to indicate some of your observations, directions and wonderings using lines, shading or colour.

SESSION SEVEN

Part One

Balance is Posture, Posture is Balance: Re-mapping 'Posture'

❾ DISCUSS

You will have noticed by now that the word balance is being used regularly in this manual. How would you describe balance? What do we mean when we say we are either 'on' or 'off' balance? How do you know if you are 'on' or 'off' balance? What positions are easier to balance in? What stages does a baby go through before standing upright?

The animal on all-fours need have little concern with balance.[18]

▭ RECALL

Think back to Session One when we looked at the force of gravity (often illustrated with a line) that is constantly acting upon us as we live on earth!
We learned that spending time laying in Semi Supine each day offers the body (in particular the spine) a moment where the compressional force of gravity (stress) is lessened.

☙ EXPLORE

Find a clear space on the floor and come into a crawling position on all fours.

Fig. 108

▭ RECALL and project the Alexander directions:

- Allow the neck to be free *so that*
- the head can go forward and up *so that*
- the back (whole torso) can lengthen and widen

---

[18] Todd, Mabel Elsworth. *The Thinking Body*, New York, Dance Horizons, 1977, p.160.

Take some time in this crawling position to observe the weight distribution. You may also like to do some crawling and notice how this weight is distributed and re-distributed in locomotion.

Then, project your directions and find a way to kneel and come up to standing on your feet. (You may like to use a stool or chair to support you in this movement).

In standing, observe the difference in how your weight is distributed. You may like to close your eyes to observe this and compare it to what you noticed when you were on all fours.

(In upright) The weights of the body, which have been distributed over a broad base through a horizontal spine and four legs, are now transferred through a vertical spine onto a narrow base and thereafter carried through two legs to the ground. Mechanically, this involves new lines of weight-thrust upon supporting bones all the way from the occiput (skull) to the ground...[19]

❾ DISCUSS

What did you notice change as you came to standing in your exploration? What do you do in order to stand up? Were there any moments when you felt 'off' balance? What did you do in response to this feeling?

▤ Write here your definition of a) 'good' posture and b) 'bad' posture:

_____
_____
_____
_____
_____
_____
_____
_____
_____
_____
_____
_____
_____
_____
_____
_____
_____
_____
_____

---

[19] Todd, Mabel Elsworth. *The Thinking Body*, New York, Dance Horizons, 1977, p.68.

⊟   Circle the picture below that best depicts your sense of what 'good' posture is and describe the reason for your choice. If none of these depict your idea of good posture, describe what this is.

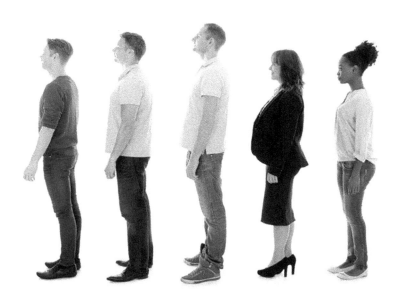

Fig. 109

When people find out that I teach the Alexander Technique, I find that many of them immediately <u>sit bolt upright</u>, <u>arch their backs</u> and <u>pull their shoulders back</u>, thinking that they have now improved their posture. *(Richard Brennan, Alexander Technique Teacher)*[20]

ෆ   EXPLORE and ❾   DISCUSS
Take it in turns in the group to demonstrate or describe some of the things you have been instructed to do in relation to posture. Some examples to get you started are:

"Roll the shoulders back and down"
"Tuck the pelvis (your bottom) under"
"Pull/suck the abdomen in"

How do these things affect the organization of the various parts of the body and your balance? Do they support us to cooperate or interfere with our design?

❾   DISCUSS
Are you aware of some of the standard Physiotherapy posture ideals being taught and published? How might you help someone understand the problems with the following guidelines?

----

[20] Brennan, Richard. *Change Your Posture, Change Your Life: How the power of the Alexander Technique can combat back pain, tension and stress*, London, Watkins Publishing, 2012, p. 54.

How to Improve Your Standing Posture

(http://physioworks.com.au/FAQRetrieve.aspx?ID=31642)

If we had to give you one tip about great standing posture it would be to "stand tall"! All the muscles that you need to push you taller are the same ones that improve your posture.

Stand tall!

Hold your head up straight with your chin in. Do not tilt your head forward, backward or sideways.

Keep your earlobes in line with the middle of your shoulders.

Keep your shoulders back, your knees straight and your back straight.

Let arms hang naturally down the sides of the body

Lightly draw in your core stomach muscles. Do not tilt your pelvis forward.

Avoid locking the knees

Ensure your feet arches are in a neutral (not flat) position.

Stand with weight mostly on the balls of the feet, not with weight on the heels.

Keep feet slightly apart, about shoulder-width.

If standing for a long period of time, shift weight from one foot to the other, or rock from heels to toes.

How to Quickly Check Your Standing Posture

Stand against a wall with shoulders and bottom touching wall. In this position, the back of the head should also touch the wall - if it does not, the head is carried to far forward (anterior head carriage).

CS EXPLORE
Look back to the picture you circled as best depicting 'good' posture.

☐ RECALL and project the Alexander directions:

- Allow the neck to be free *so that*
- the head can go forward and up *so that*
- the back (whole torso) can lengthen and widen

Now simply *think* back to that picture and *'be'* that picture of 'good' posture.
Observe how this is, in particular how much effort or ease is required to adopt it.

Continue to stand and now instruct yourself to *'stand with good posture'* or to *do* one of the just discussed posture instructions i.e. pull your shoulders back and down.
Again, observe how this is, in particular how much effort or ease is required to adopt it.

❾ DISCUSS
What did you observe during your explorations? Were you surprised by the effort or lack thereof required to adopt your chosen image of 'good' posture? How important was your thinking in relation to adopting this image of 'good' posture?

Given what you have discovered, do you think the labels 'good' and 'bad' are helpful in relation to posture? Was your experience of adopting the image of 'good' posture a static or dynamic experience? Was there a concrete moment when it was 'good'?

A correct position or posture indicates a fixed position, and a person held to a fixed position cannot grow, as we understand growth. The correct position today cannot be the correct position a week later...
(F.M. Alexander) [21]

▢ RECALL
Think back to Session One when we covered *how* we project the Alexander directions for Primary Control. Also think back to Session Two, Part Four when we examined how the *language* we use to instruct ourselves directly influences the quality of our response i.e. *'brace' versus 'activate' the muscles of the pelvic floor.*

We can see that our choice of language and how we use this language to instruct others and ourselves is very important.

With this in mind, contemplate and **❾   DISCUSS** the following:

Considering my habitual response to hearing the word posture, is it really a useful one for me?
Does my idea of posture correlate with the following description:

Posture is far more complex than just standing or sitting up straight; it can be described as the way in which we support and balance our bodies against the ever-present force of gravity while we go about our daily activities.[22]

---

[21] Alexander, F.M. *Constructive Conscious Control of the Individual,* Mouritz, London, 1923 (2000), p. 174.

[22] Brennan, Richard. *Change Your Posture, Change Your Life: How the power of the Alexander Technique can combat back pain, tension and stress*, London, Watkins Publishing, 2012, p. 54.

What other word/s could I use to describe posture that correlate with this description?

Since by definition posture means stasis or standing perfectly still (according to its roots positura and ponere), and for most of us it is enveloped in a lifetime of (oftentimes) misleading instruction, we will do well to find an alternative – to re-map the word posture.

Balance is a powerful substitute for posture as it well describes the ever-changing, dynamic organization of the biped human design.

Fig. 110   Fig. 111

Part Two

The Forgotten Senses: Kinesthesia and Proprioception

❾ DISCUSS
How many senses do we have? What are the sense organs and where are they located?

☙ EXPLORE
To begin to tune into your kinesthesic sense, you can try this:

In sitting or standing raise one of your hands over your head where you can't see it. Do you notice that even though you can't see your hand, you feel that you know exactly where it is? Keep the hand here and wiggle your fingers. Again, do you notice that you have a sense of what you are doing with the hand even though you can't see it? You likely have some sense of the location, speed and range of your finger movement.
Now, bring your hand down to in front of you, where you can see it and wiggle you fingers here. Do you notice how now that you have the visual sense (you can see it) the kinesthetic sense fades?

Kinesthesia (from kinema - movement and thesia - perception) is the perception or sense we have of our body in motion. It is this sense that gives us information about how we are moving, where we are moving and the quality of this movement.

Proprioception (from proprius – one's own and percepio – perception) is the same as kinesthesia but in the strict sense refers to our sense of how we are organized in space when we are stationary.

ⓘ Kinesthesia and proprioception are often used interchangeably. Bearing in mind that we are never entirely still or stationary, even when standing on the spot relatively 'still', we will use kinesthesia from here on to refer to this sense.

❾ DISCUSS
Why is our kinesthetic sense important? Consider an individual with a hearing or visual impairment. How might the dependence upon kinesthesia be different for these individuals?

The kinesthetic sense uses <u>input receptors from within the muscles and joints</u>; it also sends messages to the brain whenever there is movement. These sensations send impulses along nerves to the brain and thus inform us of any movement that the body is making, even the movement of breathing.[23]

ଔ EXPLORE
Come into standing, and take a walk. Purposely tighten your neck and walk like this for a little while. Then, give your Alexander directions and walk again. Pay attention to the difference in how much or little you are able to register what is happening kinesthetically.

☐ RECALL and ➒ DISCUSS
Think back to Session One and how we use the process of projecting our directions to establish the Primary Control.
In your exploration just now, you were essentially <u>interfering</u> with the Primary Control – the dynamic and balanced organization of the head, neck and torso.
How did interfering with the Primary Control impact upon your senses? In particular how was your kinesthetic sense impacted?

The information our brain is receiving or our interpretation of this information from any of the senses can be faulty if it is in some way being interfered with, contradicted or affected.

☐ If, *the kinesthetic sense uses <u>input receptors from within the muscles and joints</u>*, we can see that the organization of our bones and muscles will directly impact upon the information received by the input receptors. In this way, the more we come into balance, into the most efficient organization of our whole structure, the more accurate, pronounced and useful our kinesthetic sense will be.

---

[23] Brennan, Richard. *Change Your Posture, Change Your Life: How the power of the Alexander Technique can combat back pain, tension and stress*, London, Watkins Publishing, 2012, p.102.

Part Three

An Obstacle: Faulty Sensory Appreciation

ᏸ EXPLORE
Repeat the following exploration from earlier:
In sitting or standing raise one of your hands over your head where you can't see it. Do you notice that even though you can't see your hand, you feel that you know exactly where it is?
Now, leave your hand exactly where it is and move your head to have a look. Is it in fact where you felt it to be?
Repeat this with the other hand.

❾ DISCUSS
We live in a society that longs after 'good' posture and more generally good health. If you are a teacher, therapist or physician of any kind, you will be well aware of this longing. In fact, your income may be quite dependent upon it!
Why do you think these ideals of 'good' posture and good health evade so many people? What do you identify as some of the obstacles in our endeavors to improve our posture and health?

Everyone wants to be right, but no one stops to consider if their idea of right is right. (F.M. Alexander)

According to Alexander, what you experienced in your earlier exploration (the disparity between what you feel and think you are doing and what you are in fact doing) is a universal phenomenon that has occurred in the process of human evolution and is a key obstacle in improving the human condition. He termed this Faulty Sensory Appreciation (FSA) and in his writings explains how this has become so. Essentially humans have not adapted adequately to the rapidly changing environments we live in and have continued to operate (in spite of these changes) in a manner that was appropriate during pre-civilization.
The restoration of our sensory appreciation is key in the improvement of our posture and health.

However, what causes FSA operates in something of a twofold, vicious cycle:

In the modern day world we are (increasingly) bombarded by stimuli directed at the five outward senses thus our engagement with our kinesthetic sense is dampened.
Most of us constantly use excess tension which over time means the kinesthetic sense cannot work efficiently, in turn becoming unreliable and giving us faulty information about what we are doing i.e. where we are in space, how we are moving.

We can't detect muscular tension and imbalance because our feedback senses are not in healthy operation. Our feedback senses are not in healthy operation because of our muscular tension and imbalance. We can't detect muscular tension and imbalance because our feedback senses are not in healthy operation. Our feedback senses are not in healthy operation because of our muscular tension and imbalance...

❾ DISCUSS
Given the described vicious cycle, how can we possibly begin the process of restoring accurate sensory appreciation, in particular the kinesthetic sense? Personally, how would this benefit you in relation to your posture and health? If you are a teacher, therapist or physician, how might this positively impact upon your work?

Almost all civilized human creatures have developed a condition in which the sensory appreciation (feeling) is more or less imperfect and deceptive, and it naturally follows that it cannot be relied upon in re-education, readjustment and co-ordination, or in our attempts to put right something we know to be wrong... (F.M. Alexander) [24]

▤ Cross out which ONE the following processes ARE NOT going to support the FIRST stages of restoring accurate sensory appreciation:

- Developing AWARENESS of when (what situations) and where (location in the body) we are using excess tension
- CONSCIOUSLY RELEASING TENSION
- PROJECTING DIRECTIONS for establishment of PRIMARY CONTROL
- INCREASING the REGULARITY of your chosen exercise activity (i.e. Pilates, yoga, gym, swimming)
- Using EXTERNAL MEANS (mirror, another person, video camera) to gain RELIABLE FEEDBACK on what you are actually doing
- Developing a detailed and accurate BODY MAP
- RELINQUISHING the need to feel RIGHT and trusting that the RIGHT thing will initially feel WRONG

ⓘ It is important to understand that even though there has been a rise is ergonomically designed furniture, equipment and training in recent years in workplaces, we tend to bring our faulty sensory appreciation to the use of this equipment and the interpretation of this training.

❾ DISCUSS

---

[24] Alexander, F.M. *Constructive Conscious Control of the Individual,* London, Mouritz, 2000 (1923), p. 150.

Look at the two signs below. What problems to you see in each of them? How might they be a byproduct of FSA in the people who have designed them? How might these be interpreted by those who read them?

Fig. 112

Now look at the picture below. What principles does it well communicate in terms good use in bending that the previous signs do not?

Fig. 113

▤ LIST and ❾   DISCUSS with a partner

Some activities you do regularly
Processes that you can begin to apply to each of these activities that will help you to develop more accurate sensory appreciation

----

The process of developing and refining our sensory appreciation is a slow one, but it can be a fascinating and very enjoyable one. We are like creatures coming out of a long sleep, who need to be treated with care and respect, but also with an awareness that our slumbers have left us short of important skills which now need to be carefully cultivated if we are to survive as a species.[25]

[25] Park, Glenn. *The Art of Changing: A New Approach to the Alexander Technique*, Bath, Ashgrove Press Limited, 1989, p. 42.

SESSION EIGHT

Part One

Muscle Function

❾ DISCUSS

What are muscles?

What is the role of muscles in our overall functioning? What do we mean when we say we 'use' our muscles? Is there a scale of muscle 'use'? What is muscle tone?

Looking back at your drawing of yourself from Session One, did you include musculature? If so, what areas or specific muscles did you include?

Muscles are responsible for all the movement of the body and in this way a basic understanding of their <u>function</u> is important to include in our Body Map.

In the broadest sense there are two different types of muscles operating in the body. These are described as Involuntary and Voluntary:

- ✓ **Involuntary muscles** contract and expand automatically and include the muscles of the heart, blood vessels, digestive system and eye mechanism. Involuntary aptly describes the way in which we cannot consciously control these muscles.
- ✓ **Voluntary/Skeletal** muscles are muscles whose contraction action we can control (the expanding part is automatic). It is these muscles that attach to and move the bones.

Skeletal) Muscles are responsible for the movement of bones. They should have the greatest freedom possible for this function and should not be called upon unnecessarily for the support of weights, still less to bear the burden of weights off center.[26]

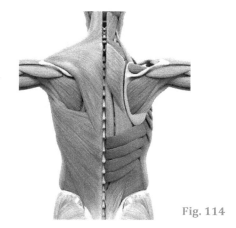

Fig. 114

---

[26] Todd, Mabel Elsworth. *The Thinking Body*, New York, Dance Horizons, 1977, p. 62.

LOOK

Each skeletal muscle is made up on hundreds of thousands of fibers, each enclosed by a protective sheath. These fibers are grouped together in bundles, which in turn are contained within a larger fibrous sack.

On this diagram, labeled from left to right is the **Fascia, Muscle Fibres, Blood Vessels.**

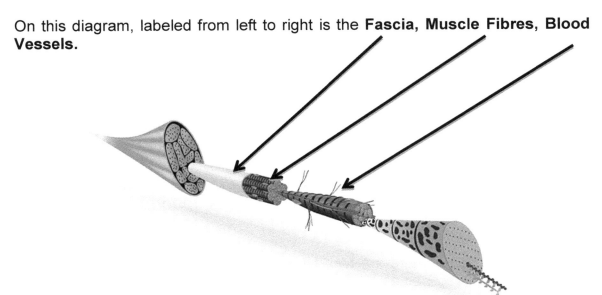

Fig. 115

(Sarcomere, Myofibril, Actin, Myosins follow if we continue along the chain to the right)

One end of the muscle sack is connected to one bone, and the other end to another bone. When the muscle contracts it becomes shorter in length and moves the bones to which it is attached usually causing a joint i.e. elbow, to move.

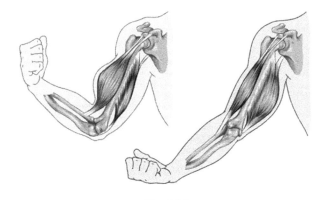

Fig. 116

Muscles contract upon receiving a stimulus from the central nervous system. Located in the spinal cord of the central nervous system are thousands of nerve cells each of which connects to several muscles fibers. When we decide to do an action i.e. lift our arm to pick up a glass of water, our decision to do this movement is communicated through the nervous system to the muscles.

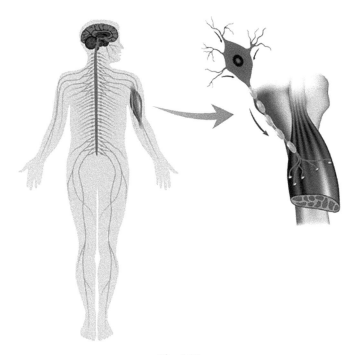

Fig. 117

The inner meat of the muscle is the flexible part that can shorten or lengthen and be tensed or released. It is the part of the muscle that has the power to generate movement. The outer sack of the muscle while also able to shorten or lengthen in relation to the inner meat is less flexible and offers more of a protective role.

ⓘ *If the meat of the muscle has become habitually shortened, the sack will shorten with it and in time will not be able to lengthen to the full stretch of the original healthy muscle. In effect the sack of the muscle shrinks to fit the habitually shortened meat of the muscle. So if the inner meat of the muscle is habitually shortened, or if a person's movement is restricted and limited, the meat of the muscle will slowly lose its freedom as the outer sack tightens up around it.*[27]

One of the objects of the Alexander Technique is to create a state of play in the meat of the muscles so that they only use the minimum necessary tension and shortening for any activity.[28]

---

[27] Park, Glenn. *The Art of Changing: A New Approach to the Alexander Technique*, Bath, Ashgrove Press Limited, 1989, p. 52.

[28] Park, Glenn. *The Art of Changing: A New Approach to the Alexander Technique*, Bath, Ashgrove Press Limited, 1989, p. 50.

EXPLORE

Get yourself a glass of water, sit down at a table and put the water down. Before having a drink, just think about *what muscles am I going to use to pick up this glass of water?*

▤ Write down your answer here:

You may have answered that question by thinking mostly about the biceps and muscles of the arm. This is true and certainly the most pronounced muscular activity involved in the action. But... it is by no means the whole picture. When you make a movement, any movement, a lot of muscles are involved. The whole picture involves ALL of the following:

1. Prime movers (the muscle or muscles directly responsible for that movement)
2. Antagonists (the muscle or muscles that oppose the prime movers by releasing)
3. Muscles stabilizing the part of the body which is moving
4. Muscles responsible for maintaining the balance of the whole body in the changing situation created by the movement ⓘ (*If I go to lift my arm to pick up this glass and I move only my arm I will unbalance and fall over. I won't be consciously aware of it but as I go to pick up this glass my calf muscles will turn on along with a whole range of other muscles through my body in order to maintain and to subtly shift my balance.*)
5. Muscles responsible for maintaining the shape of the body, the integrity of the structure
6. You also need to inhibit, consciously or unconsciously muscular activity, which will interfere with the movement you are making. (e.g. tightening your neck as you go to raise your arm)

In other words, virtually every muscle of the body will be involved in virtually every movement we make!

114

ⓘ We can also add to the above 'full picture' the following details:

- ✓ Muscles can play different roles and rapidly change roles according to circumstances
- ✓ Muscle activity is altered according to whether the movement is gravity assisted or not
- ✓ Each individual nerve ending controls only a section of the fibers of the whole muscle and in this way some or all of the fibers may participate in the movement

ଔ EXPLORE

Now sitting at the table, think about the 'whole picture' we have just painted.
⬜ RECALL and project the Alexander directions:

- Allow the neck to be free *so that*
- the head can go forward and up *so that*
- the back (whole torso) can lengthen and widen

so that you can pick up and have a drink of your water.

▤ Write down a 'whole picture' observation of this activity. What movement and tensions happened in muscles NOT at the arm? What parts of you were you most aware of? Least aware of?

Does this 'whole picture' awareness make you more curious about how you do even the simplest day-to-day activity? Can you detect how the projection of your Alexander directions to establish the Primary Control impacts upon the 'whole picture'?

Part Two

Muscles Types and Imbalances

So far we have touched upon the very complex nature of what occurs in the muscles when we undertake any activity. It is apparent that it would be far too difficult, impossible even, to try to control so many interdependent details. The fact is that we all have a system of reflexes operating continually to organize the whole system of muscular activity. In order to look at this reflex system, it is important to firstly understand the two very different types and thus roles of muscles operating within the muscular system.

What muscles do I use predominantly to maintain my uprightness – to maintain my balance – to maintain the integrity of my structure?

▤   Write your answer here:

❾   DISCUSS

What you have answered to this question depends very much upon your habitual way of maintaining upright posture and your sense (accurate or not) of what this is.

Discuss what you wrote down and the variations among the group.

☐   RECALL the earlier description of Involuntary and Voluntary/Skeletal muscles.

The Voluntary or Skeletal muscles contain two types of muscle fibers, a predominance of which determines the muscle type:

✓   White, fast twitch muscle fibers which provide strength for bursts of activity for short periods of time = **Phasic Muscles**

✓   Red slow-twitch muscle fibers which can keep on working over long periods of time without tiring = **Postural Muscles**

Given this information, it makes sense that the muscles which we **predominately** want to be using to maintain upright posture and support our movement are the **Postural Muscles** - rich in the slow-twitch fibers and able to work for long periods without tiring. However, what we frequently see and experience is that the **Phasic** or "movement" muscles are being overused in an attempt to keep us upright.

Postural Muscles	Phasic Muscles
Designed to keep us upright	Designed to perform actions
Support us and keep us balanced against the force of gravity	Used to perform movements
Predominance of red muscle fibres	Predominance of white muscle fibres
Contract more slowly, 'slow twitch'	Contract quickly, 'fast twitch'
Fatigue resistant, take a long time to tire	Tire quickly
Activated by postural reflexes	Activated by conscious mind

ભ EXPLORE
To experience how the phasic muscles tire quickly, try this:
Hold your arm out to the side at 90 degrees to your body. Continue to hold it there as you tire and observe what you do at the arm and elsewhere in your body in order to continue to hold your arm up.

Fig. 118

ⓘ Commonly the more superficial extensor muscles in the sacrospinalis or erector spinae group (Phasic) of the spine are massively over-activated. When people go for massage therapy these muscles are palpably like concrete or ropes! They have lost their quality of suppleness and resilience as they are being made to do much more work they were ever designed to do. The consequence of this over-activation is that the deeper, first layer of the back - transversospinalis (i.e. Multifidus) and sub-occipital (i.e. Rectus Capitus) muscles, eventually fail to engage appropriately. This deep, central support becomes lazy and virtually dis-engaged.

ⓘ The habit of overusing the movement and superficial muscles is of particular interest in working with people with pain syndromes like Fibromyalgia where there is an over sensitisation of the nervous system and they have very little endurance. For them this extra unnecessary muscular contraction is very quickly felt as pain, and the overall extra work being done as fatigue.

ભ EXPLORE
Sitting in your chair, have a slump or assume what you consider to be 'bad' posture. Now come out of that by deliberately sitting up straight.
Repeat this a couple of times and observe what muscles you use to come out of the slump. Also observe with what quality you engage these muscles.
Also, have a look around the group at what other people are doing to come out of their slump.

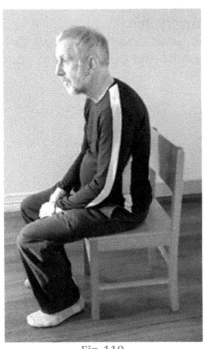

Fig. 119

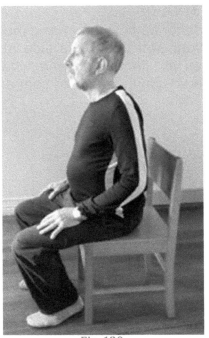

Fig. 120

Quite universally, we will try to improve our posture using phasic muscles rather than postural muscles. Just now, you have probably been using the superficial back/neck, abdominal and shoulder/arm muscles to sit up straight out of your slump. You may even identify that you alternate between slumping and this kind of 'sitting up' when you have to be in a chair for an extended period of time. Neither option is sustainable and you continually seek a more comfortable way of maintaining this upright organization.

Even if with the best of intentions we try to improve our posture and overall balance using the phasic muscles, we will repeatedly fail. Over time this engagement of the phasic muscles deeply fatigues them, leading to immobility and eventually musculoskeletal problems.

❾ DISCUSS
Given what we have explored and discussed so far, how can we go about developing good posture – good posture being a sustainable, balanced upright organization in accordance with our design? What muscles would you hypothesise need to be recruited? How might this be done?

… by applying the Alexander principles, we can employ our thinking abilities to elicit our postural reflexes and to refrain from using the phasic muscles to support us, and making our posture more natural.
(Dr Miriam Wohl, Alexander Teacher and Medical Doctor)

Fig. 121

cs EXPLORE

Come back to the exploration in the chair. Assume the slumped posture once more. Now ☐ RECALL and project the Alexander directions:

- Allow the neck to be free *so that*
- the head can go forward and up *so that*
- the back (whole torso) can lengthen and widen

As you continue to project these directions, just think about how you might come to sit in a more balanced upright way using the least possible engagement of the phasic muscles. Once you have a clear conception, again project your direction and move yourself out of the slump.

You may like to try this a few times, prior to discussing with the group.

❾ DISCUSS

What did you observe in this exploration? Was it possible to use less gross muscular engagement? How important was the clarity of your thinking?

What you have just experienced, is a taste[29] of what an Alexander Teacher will manually guide you through in a lesson – the process of reducing the amount of tension you habitually engage in the phasic muscles, SO THAT the postural muscles will automatically start to engage and support us in the way they are designed. Alexander regularly expressed this key as,

"When you stop doing the wrong thing, the right thing does itself." (F.M. Alexander)

---

[29] You cannot entirely conceive of and thus experience a new/alternate way to come out of a slump, that is not your habitual way, without the guidance of a teacher because, as we covered in Session Seven your sensory appreciation conditions your conception and in all of us this is more or less faulty.

Part Three

Reflexes and restoration of muscular imbalance

reflex /re·flex/ (re´fleks) a reflected action or movement; the sum total of any particular automatic response mediated by the nervous system

❾ DISCUSS
How would you describe reflex, in the context of activity in the human body?
What might Alexander be referring to when he says, "When you stop doing the wrong thing, the right thing does itself"?
What sorts of things elicit reflexive activity?

The term arc is used to describe the three processes involved in typical reflex activity. A reflex arc consists of:

1. Sensory receptor - detects stimulus (termed: afferent arm of reflex)
2. Interneurons - receive inputs from sensory receptors and synapse on motor neurons; effects on motor neurons can be excitatory or inhibitory; not present in monosynaptic reflexes
3. Motor neurons - (termed efferent arm of reflex) produce muscle contraction, motor response.

Reflexes are considered a valuable tool for clinical evaluation of nervous system function. This is because for a reflex to occur, all elements must be functional and the pathways must be intact. If reflexes are absent, a physician can diagnose where a pathway is interrupted; if reflexes are abnormal, he or she can diagnose where function is compromised. Reflexes are evaluated according to amount (size, magnitude) of motor response and latency (time to elicit motor response).

❾ DISCUSS
What are some of the reflex 'checks' you have experienced when treated by a physician i.e. GP?

Some reflexes are protective and relatively constant; i.e. Pupillary light reflex, while others are relatively constant under the same, controlled circumstances; i.e. Monosynaptic stretch reflex.

Reflexes can be modulated by the central nervous system - they can be changed or blocked in some behaviors.

Dorland's medical dictionary lists 335 reflexes, which are in operation during some part or all of our life. In this Body Mapping course we are particularly interested in the system of reflexes known as the Postural Reflexes.

Postural reflexes are automatic movements that control the equilibration we require when upright, moving and having to combat the effects of gravity. They maintain posture, balance and fluidity of movement and replace the primitive reflexes in a sequential manner as we develop. As an adult the primitive reflexes inhibit. The first postural reflex to emerge is the head-righting reflex on a vertical plane. At birth the baby has no head control, they then develop conscious control to lift their head; lowering the head at that stage is more difficult. Eventually this movement becomes automatic so that the head remains centrally aligned on top of the body with the crown uppermost. Tip a newborn upside down and their head will just hang, tip a 12-week-old baby and the head will extend backwards so that the crown is uppermost. Over time this ability to maintain head position develops on all planes.[30]

If we begin to lose our balance, we are designed such that the postural reflexes will automatically activate, without conscious involvement. This process is controlled by a complex interplay between the sensory vestibular systems; in the inner ear, the cerebellum and motor nerves controlling the muscles.

The problem is that most adults have developed habits of holding excess muscular tension that interferes with this natural process of reflex activation.

⬭ RECALL
Point to the location of your AO joint, where the skull rests upon the top cervical vertebrae. How much does the head weigh? Think about how this weight is distributed, given that the head is not a symmetrical sphere.

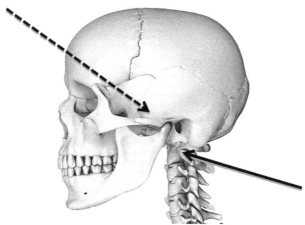

Fig. 122

Centre of Gravity

AO joint/ point of balance

➝

The head is actually set off-balance on top of the spine – the balance point and center of gravity are not in the same location.

---

[30] Sue Hyland, *Primitive Reflexes,* Retrieved 8 May 2013 from <http://suehyland.co.uk/ond/primitive-reflexes/>

✂ EXPLORE
What happens to the head when we fall asleep while sitting upright? Explore this now while sitting in your seat. Imagine you are drifting off to sleep. What muscles do you let go of or relax? Also try exploring the action of drifting off and catching yourself, as if you're on the train and don't actually want to fall asleep. What do you do?

❾ DISCUSS
What did you find? Which way did your head tend to fall? Could you detect a subtle reflexive response being activated to bring your head back into balance?

This rather curious design wherein the pivot point of the head on spine is situated <u>behind</u> the center of gravity, means that when the surrounding muscles of the neck are free the head will move slightly forward and lighten up at the AO joint. Once the head moves in this way, and providing there is freedom in the other major joints of the body, the whole system of reflex activity will spring into operation and the entire musculature, in particular the postural muscles, assume a toned quality. It is for this reason that Alexander called the head, neck, back relationship the Primary Control – it furnishes the way for organization and availability through the whole body.

☐ RECALL and 🗒 Write the Alexander Directions here:

Are these directions about increasing or releasing muscular tension? How do we DO or PROJECT these directions?

🗒 Draw on this picture to indicate the trajectory of the head movement when we free the muscles of the neck.

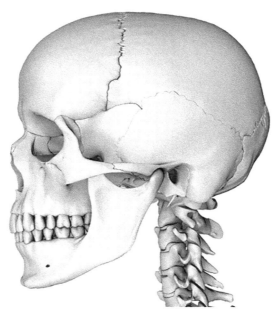

Fig. 123

122

❾ DISCUSS

What area of the body do many people have regularly massaged? What kind of tension is responsible for many headaches and eyestrain in the workplace? What area of the body is listed first on most massage 'menu's'?

It would seem that quite universally we hold a lot of tension through the neck and upper back and are thus, constantly interfering with the Primary Control. This tension or excessive contraction of the neck muscles pulls the head off balance (usually back and down) and we cease to be cooperating with our design and our relationship to gravity.

The ability to improve a pattern of support and movement for the reduction of mechanical stresses comes, <u>not through the development of bulk and power in the individual muscles</u>, but from the study and appreciation of the human body as a weight bearing and weight moving structure. Kinesthesia… is the important source of our information. Through it we are better able to bring about a better balancing of parts, and thus coordination of the whole.[31]
Loose talk about 'moving in a relaxed way' does not help anyone – it only encourages muddled thinking and hence muddles action. …this kind of talk has lead countless people into serious physical difficulties, by giving them the idea that they can somehow accomplish things by making themselves go all floppy.[32]

ೞ EXPLORE and ❾ DISCUSS

1. What happens when you get a fright? With a partner explore this by taking it in turns to create a sudden, loud noise without warning in close proximity to your partner. (A balloon can be useful for this exercise)

   What happens to the head neck relationship? Can you detect how this tension created a type of freeze/stop or break through your whole body? (Startle reflex)

   This type of contraction perfectly protects us if we are in actual danger (i.e. the honk of a car horn while crossing in the path of a vehicle).

2. Now explore, what happens when you are sitting or standing up and feeling extremely tired or unwell.

   What happens in this instance to the head neck relationship? How does this impact of the musculature through your whole body?

---

[31] Todd, Mabel Elsworth. *The Thinking Body*, New York, Dance Horizons, 1977, p. 33.
[32] Langford, Elizabeth. *Mind and Muscle,* Holand, Garant Publishing, 1999, pp. 39-40.

Fig. 124   Fig. 125   Fig. 126   Fig. 127

These days the majority of bodywork modalities are responding to the effects of increasingly inefficient use of ourselves on a day-to-day basis. Excessive contraction is an obstacle to efficiency. And yet, when we think about the physiology of how muscles work most efficiently, we will note that:

...the most effective contraction is made when the muscle concerned is already slightly stretched to begin with.

In this way, floppy 'relaxed' muscles are also an obstacle to efficiency. The fact is, balanced musculature is stretched a little, but not too much, lively and ready to reflexively spring into action.

Tools we are developing in this course to support balanced musculature:

The role of body mapping in restoring balance of the framework attached to which are the muscles, that with our kinesthetic sense we can increasingly monitor tension

The impacts of your own balanced use on your touch including diagnosis and communication with the nervous system.

Fig. 128

ⓘ WEIGHT LIFTER

Culturally in our society there has been a real emphasis on developing the superficial muscles. If we look at the weight lifter here we can see how his whole postural support is compromised in the process of developing his large superficial muscles. We can see this by, how through his whole torso he is tightening, collapsing and contracting himself. I should add that it is possible to do this type of exercise whilst bringing coordination to the whole body, and if it is done in this way you will also work at strengthening the whole body including the postural muscles.

Part Four

Mapping Muscles to understand and address specific mis-use

‎ EXPLORE

As well as mapping our skeletal structure, it is important to have a sense of the organisation and functioning of the major muscles of the body. When we are working as teachers we will likely need to respond to someone who speaks of a specific area of muscle soreness i.e. "my trapezius or upper back hurts after a long day… is there anything I can do?" This question offers a wonderful starting point for wondering why these muscles would be tiring in a person. How is it that they are using themselves either in general or in a specific activity that would cause this? What are the muscles in question intended to do? Is this what they are being used for in this person?

▤ LABEL

Take some time to look, research and label the muscles in the series of images on the following pages.

You can use The Anatomy Colouring Book (Kapit W., Elson L.M., USA, Benjamin Cummings Publishers, 2002.), Anatomy of Movement (Calais-Germain, Blandine. Seattle, Eastland Press, 1999.) Anatomy of the Moving Body: A Basic Course in Bones, Muscles and Joints (Dimon, Theodore Jr. California, North Atlantic Books, 2008.) Body in Motion: Its Evolution and Design (Dimon, Theodore Jr. California, North Atlantic Books 2011).

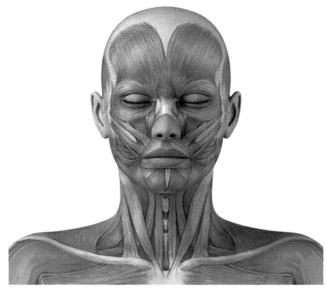

Fig. 129

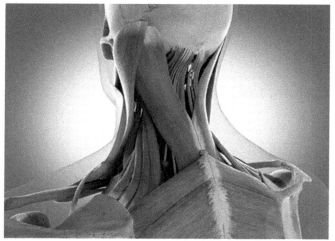

Fig. 130

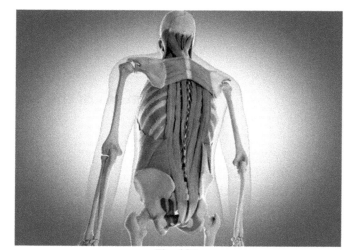

Fig. 131

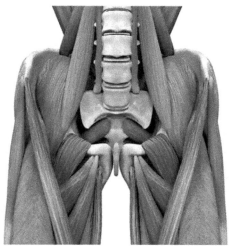

Fig. 132

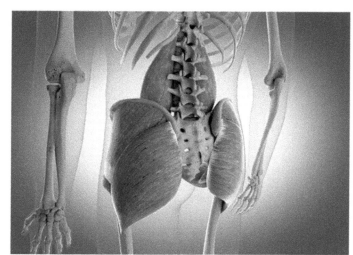

Fig. 133

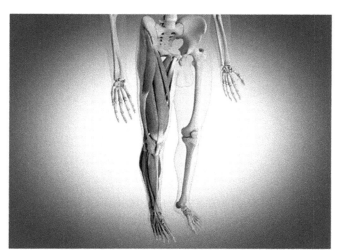

Fig. 134

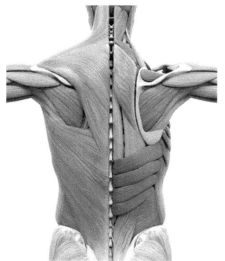

Fig. 135

SESSION NINE

Part One

Structures of the Skull: Cranium, Jaw, Tongue

❾ DISCUSS

Look back at your drawing from Session One. How did you draw your head? In particular, what shape is it? How did you draw the jaw and mouth area? How did you go about locating the nose, eyes, ears and mouth?

The skull is made up of the cranium and the face. It is the cranium that houses the brain and balancing mechanisms and possesses openings for the ears as well as part of the structure of the jaw joint.

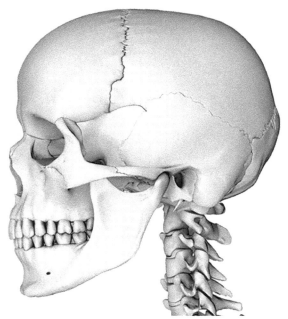

Fig. 136

Let's begin looking at the cranium part of the skull. The cranium is made up of the parietal, temporal, sphenoid, ethmoid and occipital bones. It is the base of the skull, formed by the occipital and temporal bones which we have looked at in previous sessions and will now return to in more detail.

☙ EXPLORE

Pass around the skull, looking and palpating the base area. Locate the large hole in the base – the foramen magnum. This is where the brain stem travels from the brain into the spinal cord. Also locate the occipital condyles; the two rounded bumps either side of the foramen magnum.

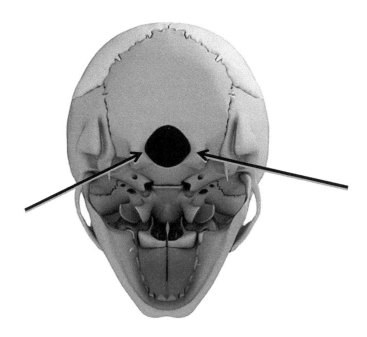

Fig. 137

Now look at the top vertebrae of the spine (atlas) and fit these two condyles on the skull into the two corresponding depressions on the spine.

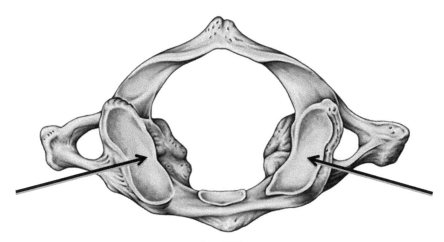

Fig. 138

☐ RECALL, and project your Alexander directions:

- Allow the neck to be free *so that*
- the head can go forward and up *so that*
- the back (whole torso) can lengthen and widen

Then in sitting or standing point to this meeting point (remembering it is somewhere between the ears), and make a small yes nodding movement.

☐ RECALL that the "no" nod happens a little lower down, between the axis and atlas or top two cervical vertebrae. This will make sense when you consider the rocker shape of the meeting of the skull and spine at the atlanto-occipital joint. Rotation movement at this level would require a different shape of joint.

...the base of the skull corresponds not with the underside of the jaw, but with the cheekbone. This is very important, because when we confuse the head with the jaw and parts of the neck, we lack a clear picture of what the head is and therefore cannot accurately "direct" the head in movement.
(Theodore Dimon Jr., *Anatomy of the Moving Body: A Basic Course in Bones, Muscles and Joints*)

❾ DISCUSS
Why might it be important to have the base of the skull, in particular the foramen magnum and the occipital condyles mapped accurately? Think about and note below the function of each of these and the consequence interference may have in these areas:

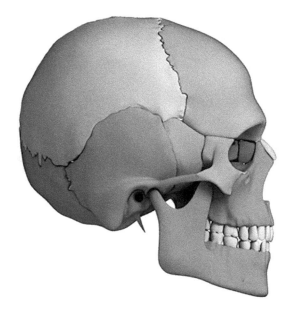

Fig. 139

The face part of the skull is made up of the nasal, turbinate, vomer, lachrymal, zygomatic, malar, palate, superior maxilla and mandible bones. All of these bones along with those of the cranium are connected by sutures. At birth the skull bones are not fully formed but gradually come to fit firmly together.

▤ On the on the previous page picture, colour/shade/indicate the mandible (jaw) bone.

We have a single jaw bone that anchors the lower teeth. It is important to note that the upper teeth are anchored in the cranium part of the skull, not a separate "upper jaw".

The jaw joint is known as the temporomandibular joint (TMJ) since it is where the temporal and mandible bones articulate. It is important that we have the location TMJ accurately mapped in terms of its location and also its movement.

ଔ EXPLORE
Lets begin by looking at the TMJ location. In pairs or alone, palpate this joint. You may find it helps to open and close your mouth in order to find this location most accurately.

The temporomandibular joint is not a simple hinge joint as we often think. More than just opening and closing, we can slide the mandible (lower jaw) forward and back and side-to-side.

ଔ EXPLORE
In pairs or alone, begin standing and looking in a mirror. Once again palpate the location of your TMJ and begin to explore the range of movement here. You may like to also stand side on to see the sliding motion forward and back.

When you have completed this exploration in standing, get some books for under your head and come into laying down in semi supine. Here, explore these movements of the TMJ again.

If time permits, you may also like to try a further different orientation, laying over an inflatable fit ball.

❾ DISCUSS

With your partner or with the group, discuss what you observed in your explorations. In particular, what did you notice in the different orientations (standing then laying down)?

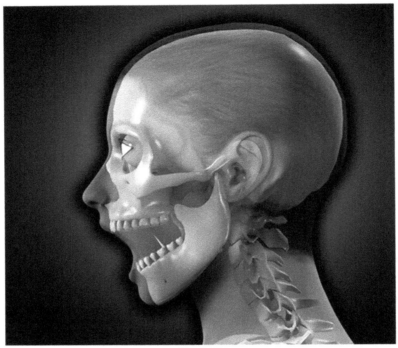

Fig. 140

ⓘ Temporomandibular joint dysfunction (sometimes abbreviated to TMD or TMJD and also termed temporomandibular joint dysfunction syndrome, temporomandibular disorder or many other names), is an umbrella term covering pain and dysfunction of the muscles of mastication (the muscles that move the jaw) and the temporomandibular joints (the joints which connect the mandible to the skull). Symptoms include pain, restricted mandibular movement, and noises from the temporomandibular joints (TMJ) during jaw movement. It is often cause by excess tension in the surrounding muscles (poor use) that over time can lead to nerve impingement. See appendix for more information and articles.

ᴄ℥ EXPLORE

In pairs or you can explore the relationship between the primary control and jaw movement.

With one person sitting and one standing behind, ☐ RECALL, and project your Alexander directions:

- Allow the neck to be free *so that*
- the head can go forward and up *so that*
- the back (whole torso) can lengthen and widen

The person standing will place their hands on the TMJ of the person sitting. The person sitting will slowly open and close their mouth.

Then, the person sitting will purposely interfere with the primary organisation by tensing their neck/pulling head back and down or pocking head forward.

Again the person standing will place their hands on the TMJ of the seated person as they slowly open and close their mouth.

Pay attention to the way in which neck tension/loss of primary organisation interferes with free movement at the TMJ.
Swap roles and repeat.

❾ DISCUSS
With your partner or in a large group discuss what you noticed in this exploration. Describe some of your observations here:

Part Two

The Upper Spine and Internal Structures

ɑ EXPLORE
With a partner sit down, project your Alexander directions and have a brief conversation on something of your choice. When you are finished pause and think about where you imagine the sound of your voice comes from and how it is that you are making this sound.

❾ DISCUSS
In a large group, describe and discuss individuals' ideas about speaking and sound making, including how they have mapped the vocal mechanism in relation to its location, size and function. Also discuss ideas around how to 'project' the voice.

Alexander observed that, as he went to begin the act of speaking, he pulled his head slightly back and down, depressing his larynx, shortening his torso, causing him to tense his legs and feet.

® If you haven't already, make sure you read Alexander's own description of what he found himself to be doing in speaking in *Use of the Self, Chapter 1.*

ɑ EXPLORE
With what has just been explored and discussed in mind, set yourself up in front of a mirror (having a mirror to the side would also be helpful if possible).

☐ RECALL, and project your Alexander directions:

- Allow the neck to be free *so that*
- the head can go forward and up *so that*
- the back (whole torso) can lengthen and widen

Begin to speak and observe yourself as you do so. Observe anything that you can see or feel in the way of tension, gripping through the neck (throat), the face, jaw, tongue, even the eyes. You may also like to palpate your jaw area as you do so.

Also, observe anything that is happening in the rest of your body, even in seemingly remote areas such as the feet. Remember what Alexander was doing with his feet as he spoke?

➒ DISCUSS and ▤Note what you have observed. Include anything you noticed, even if you don't yet have a sense of why this is happening or what you might do to change it.

Changing habits requires Attention and Intention

Lets now come back to the question of, how do we make sound or speak? What are the key structures involved in vocalization?

ෆ EXPLORE

In sitting, place your hands lightly on the front of your neck and swallow. Can you feel something moving? If so, you have just located your larynx, the key structure of vocalization.

The larynx located at the front of the neck attaches to the top of the trachea (the tube through which air moves). It is also suspended from the hyoid bone (located at the base of the tongue). The larynx comprises mostly of cartilage and muscle and is quite small, around the size of a walnut.

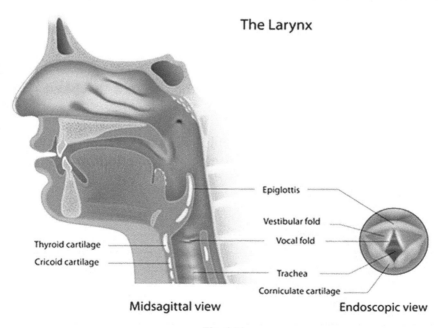

The Larynx

Epiglottis

Vestibular fold

Vocal fold

Thyroid cartilage

Cricoid cartilage

Trachea

Corniculate cartilage

Midsagittal view   Endoscopic view

Fig. 141

135

❾ DISCUSS
Why might it be important to have the larynx and surrounding areas mapped in your body map?

Misconceptions or mis-mappings of the larynx can interfere with phonation and cause persistent hoarseness or sore throat through straining to get the sound out.

ᚑᛒ EXPLORE
Once again, place your hand lightly on the front of the neck on what you now know to be your larynx. This time hum a little. You will be able to feel a slight vibration as you do this.

The vibration you have just experienced is the vocal folds housed with the larynx, coming together and vibrating at the same time as air is passing through, in order to make sound or phonate.

ⓘ It is important to understand that without your hands on your larynx, you cannot feel this mechanism working when you speak, hum or sing. What we can feel are the surrounding neck muscles. This is why we often engage the neck muscles in order to 'project' our voice or make a 'better' sound. We need to remember and trust that all movement of phonation occurs WITHOUT the help of the neck muscles.

In order for the larynx to function according to its design, we need to be in a balanced organization. Attending to the primary control will indirectly but certainly support optimal functioning of the larynx.

ᚑᛒ EXPLORE
Come into standing. ▭ RECALL, and project your Alexander directions:

- Allow the neck to be free *so that*
- the head can go forward and up *so that*
- the back (whole torso) can lengthen and widen

Begin to hum. Continue to hum and lift the chin so that the head is off balance. Bring the head back into balance and then poke the head forward. Continue to hum and now drop the chin down.
Experiment with the combination of humming and these movements and listen to the sound changes. Also observe any tension you feel when the head is not in balance.

▤ On this picture, shade or outline the tongue. As you do so, consider how you think about your tongue, in particular its size and it's attachment.

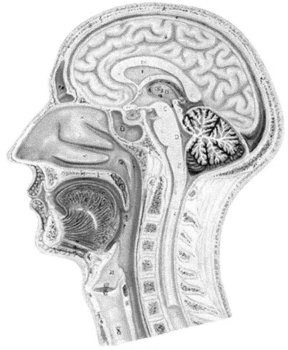

Fig. 142

Commonly we think of the tongue as just the part we can see when we open our mouths. However, as is clear in this picture, it is a rather large muscle occupying significant space in the head.

The tongue is used to move food around and assist to push it down into the stomach. In communication, the tongue is used to articulate the vowels and consonants. While the tip area is very sensitive (area of the taste buds) the rest of the tongue is easy to ignore as we cannot feel it as clearly.
As you can see in the picture, the tongue originates behind the chin with the fibres extending back to the hyoid bone. The fibres of the visible part of the tongue are curled up and forward in order to form the back, blade (sides) and tip area. It is interesting to note that the base of the tongue is well below the roots of the teeth.

Come into balanced standing. ☐ RECALL, and project your Alexander directions:

- Allow the neck to be free *so that*
- the head can go forward and up *so that*
- the back (whole torso) can lengthen and widen

Firstly, just think about what you have just learned about the tongue. Move it around a little. See if you can detect any tension in it. Perhaps say a couple of times, *la, la, la* or *blah, blah, blah*. Then try making a sound that requires a different engagement of the tongue such as *ta, ta, ta* and *the, the, the.*

Having experienced the tongue moving with freedom and ease, you are now going to experiment with the effect of a tense tongue.

Begin by pressing the tongue into the roof of your mouth. Notice the effect of this on your overall balance and breathing. Next, try holding or retracting the tongue, so it is sitting more toward your throat. Again, notice the effect. Then, press the tongue into the back of the lower teeth and once again notice what happens.

❾ DISCUSS and ▤Note what you observed during this exploration.
In particular, think about the negative impact tongue tension has and just how unaware we may be of this tension.

Part Three

Review of respiration and connection to phonation

We have now mapped the Larynx and understand (in simple terms) that sound is the result of air passing through this mechanism. We also understand that we shape our mouth and tongue in order to give this sound articulation.

Having this new or deepened awareness, let's return to and revise the respiratory system as covered in Session Two.

Breathing is a movement that occurs throughout the whole torso in an organized, wave-like manner.

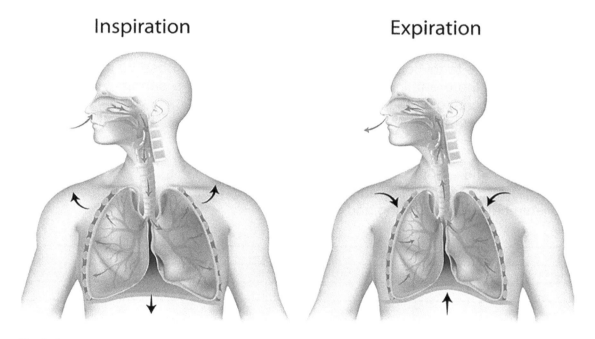

Fig. 143

On Inhalation the intercostal (muscles between ribs) and diaphragm (dome shaped muscle) contract and the whole torso gathers (top to bottom) dragging the diaphragm's central tendon downwards. This decent of the diaphragm pushes on the abdominal and pelvic contents and moves the pelvic wall out (front, sides and back) and pelvic floor down.

On Exhalation the whole torso lengthens slightly, the ribs move down and in and the diaphragm ascends, during which the pelvic floor and abdominal wall spring back.

૭ EXPLORE

Come into standing and ▭ RECALL, and project your Alexander directions:

- Allow the neck to be free *so that*
- the head can go forward and up *so that*
- the back (whole torso) can lengthen and widen

Working with a partner or alone begin by placing your hands on either side of the torso around the ribs so that you can feel the movement of breathing. Breath normally and simply follow the expansion of the ribs laterally on inhalation and the returning of the swinging back in and down on the exhalation. As you follow this add details such as the movement of the diaphragm and the spine. Can you sense these movements?
Swap roles if working with a partner and repeat.

Once again, working with your partner or alone begin by projecting your Alexander directions, coming into balanced standing and then placing hands lightly on your own or partners torso at the ribs. The person with the hands on them will begin to speak, perhaps describing what they had for breakfast that day (something simple to think of). Together you are looking to observe if speaking in any way affects the breathing, and if so in what way. If time permits you can also experiment with changing the volume of your voice.
Swap roles and repeat before discussing your observations.

❾ DISCUSS and ▤Note
With the group or in pairs, discuss what you observed, in particular the relationship between breathing and speaking.

As we learned in the introduction to this unit, Frederick Matthias Alexander was an actor and very intently experimented with the manner of use or organization he brought to the act of speaking. What he discovered in himself was that when he spoke he pulled his head back and down, depressing the larynx, sucking the air in, hollowing the back and tensing the legs and feet. He found that these things were more pronounced when he spoke loudly or endeavored to project his voice and while they were less apparent when he spoke softly, they were still very much present. In fact even when he thought about going to speak (without actually speaking), he would engage this pattern of misuse. What he also observed was that he brought this same pattern of use to all kind of activities, not only speaking.

Every time one speaks or sings a very complex mechanism is brought into action, the vocal apparatus. When having the idea of speaking, the body mechanisms will be prepared for action, they won't be activated unless the idea of speaking or singing becomes concrete, but never the less the body patterns will be awakened.[33]

Fig. 144

Alexander developed and engaged a procedure called the "whispered ah" in order to address patterns of misuse brought to the act of speaking.

cs EXPLORE
Get yourself some books for under your head, (a yoga mat to lay on if needed) and come to lay in semi supine as covered in Session One of this unit. Once you are here your trainer will take you through the Whispered Ah that is also described here[34]:

---

[33] Dias, Georgia, *Voice work in the Alexander Technique,* *http://alexandertechnique.com/articles/Voice%20work%20in%20the%20A.T.pdf retrieved 30th Sep 2013.*

[34] Description of Whisphered Ah adapted from Hilary King sited at http://www.hilaryking.net/alexander-technique/notes-on-using-the-whispered-'ah'-procedure.html retrieved 30th Sep 2013.

Whispered Ah

Say 'no' to any urge to perform the whispered 'Ah' before you have given yourself directions to free your neck, allow your head to go forward and up and allow your back to lengthen and widen. Alexander asked pupils to give directions '*one at a time and altogether*' throughout any procedure.

The first requirement in order to perform the whispered 'Ah' procedure, ideally, is to think of something amusing so that you smile or laugh in a natural manner. This frees the facial muscles and diaphragm, plus lifts the soft palette in the mouth. A forced smile will tend to tighten facial and neck muscles, not free them.

Next, let the tongue drop down behind the front teeth, allowing it to become softer and so free your tongue, right down into your throat.

Then, inhibit the urge to move without thought, give yourself directions and take care not to contract the head back and down, as you free the jaw and allow it to open in a slightly forwards direction. Do not force the jaw forwards but equally, take care to inhibit any tendency to pull it open by contracting the jaw down and in towards your throat.

As your jaw freely opens, whisper an 'Ah' sound on the outward breath, allowing your lungs to empty as you do so. Inhibit and take care not to contract down or force the air out but keep reminding yourself to have a free neck, tongue and throat, whilst you allow your body to lengthen and widen. It may help to remember that as the air is expelled out, it flows upwards through your body.

Close your mouth without tightening your jaw. Inhibit any urge to force an intake of air or interfere with the natural process of inhaling - just allow your breath to enter through your nose and let it fill your lungs.

Fig. 145

142

Part Four

Putting it together: mapping the spatial relationships of head and neck structures

▤   On this picture map in the following relationships.

Begin by circling the Atlanto-Occiptal (AO) joint
Then, draw lines from the AO joint radiating out to the following:

✓ Mouth
✓ Tip of nose
✓ Eyes
✓ Ear
✓ Top of head
✓ Base of occiput
✓ Chin

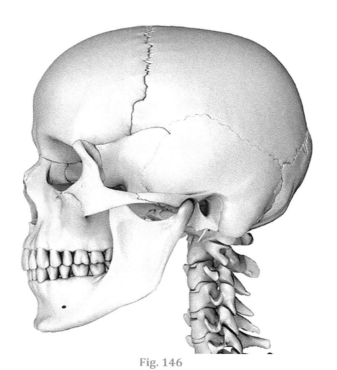

Fig. 146

SESSION TEN

Part One

Internal Organs, Superficial Musculature and Referred Pain: an overview

In the previous sessions we have mapped the major bones, joints and some structures of the body. While the mapping of the musculature will be covered in the next ten session unit: *Body Mapping for improved movement and posture 2,* here we can lightly map both the internal organs and groups of musculature so that you are left with a comprehensive starting place from which to build.

▤   On the scan diagram, map in the following internal organs:
Stomach, Liver, Spleen, Pancreas, Lungs, Heart, Kidneys (Left & Right), Ureter, Rectum, Bladder, Ascending and Descending Colon, Transverse Colon, Brain

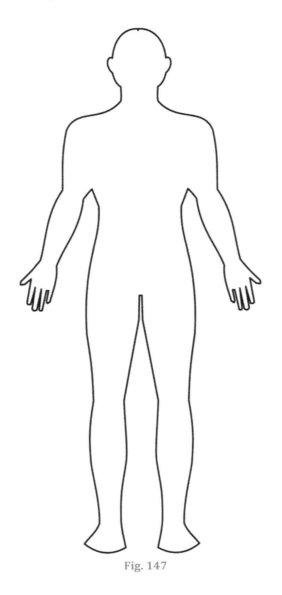

Fig. 147

Often, we have mapped our organs as located in front of the spine and as a generalized sack within us. The reality is that some organs are nestled in along the sides of the spine. There is no empty space in the torso, that being the abdominal cavity and the pelvis. If we compress our spine (lose our primary organisation) the organs have nowhere to move to and get squeezed. The abdomen may be pushed out the front.

ര EXPLORE
Come into standing side on to a mirror, or so that you can see yourself especially the torso. Look at yourself as you are, especially noting the abdominal area. Then, ☐ RECALL, and project your Alexander directions:

- Allow the neck to be free *so that*
- the head can go forward and up *so that*
- the back (whole torso) can lengthen and widen

Now have another look at yourself. Has any change occurred through the abdomen? Is it collapsed, lifted, protruding/hanging out or toned?

Now (and being careful as you do so), interfere with your primary control by either pulling the head back and down or poking it forward. Again, have a look in the mirror and observe any change this has caused in the torso, especially the abdomen.

Alexander wrote about this displacement of the internal organs that occurs when we are not in balanced organisation through the whole. It was his belief that this displacement compromised the functioning of the organs and the system as a whole and was the cause of many common ailments including digestive problems.

Many years ago the late Dr. Murdoch of Bexhill, a pupil of Alexander, took a meal of bismuth[35] and put himself in front of an x-ray screen at one of the London hospitals. It was seen that when he dis-coordinated himself, peristalsis through the gut slowed down to almost stop, whereas when he re-coordinated himself peristalsis started off again at a normal rate.
(Patrick Macdonald, The Alexander Technique As I See It, p. 7)

---

[35] Bismuth is a chemical element with symbol Bi and atomic number 83. Bismuth, a pentavalent poor metal, chemically resembles arsenic and antimony. Elemental bismuth may occur naturally, although its sulfide and oxide form important commercial ores.

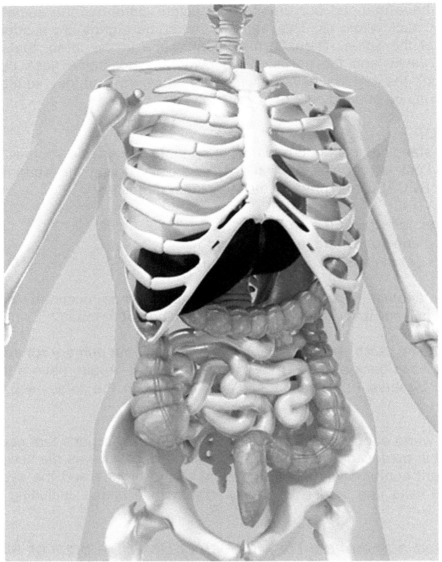

Fig. 148

↵ LATER You might like to explore and integrate the mapping of your internal organs while you are laying in semi supine. You want to particularly have a sense of the depth and breadth of the torso housing all these structures and the way in which the ongoing movement of breathing offers something of an 'internal massage' to the whole torso, so long as we are not holding tension.

ⓘ   It is important to be aware that organs can refer pain to seemingly disparate part of the body as indicated on the diagram below. This is known as referred pain. Referred pain, also called reflective pain, is pain perceived at a location other than the site of the painful stimulus. An example is the case of ischemia brought on by a myocardial infarction (heart attack), where pain is often felt in the neck, shoulders, and back rather than in the chest, the site of the injury. Referred pain is due to the fact that nerve signals from several areas of the body may "feed" the same nerve pathway leading to the spinal cord and brain.

146

Referred pain chart

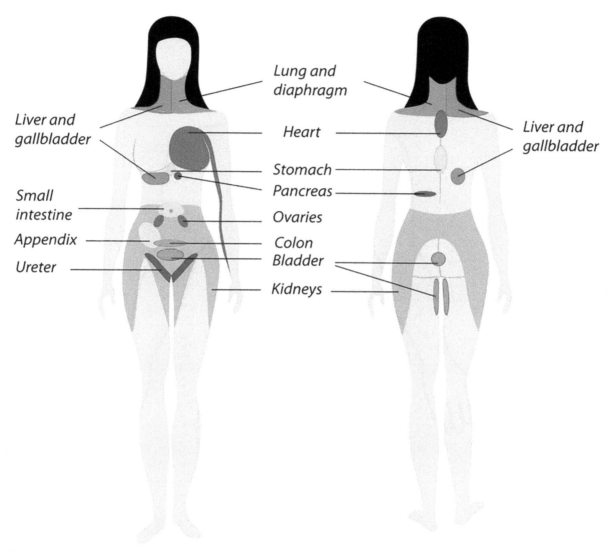

Lung and
diaphragm

Liver and
gallbladder

Heart

Liver and
gallbladder

Stomach

Small
intestine

Pancreas

Appendix

Ovaries

Ureter

Colon

Bladder

Kidneys

Fig. 149

☰ Now, on the following scan diagrams you can draw in the large groups of superficial muscles through the limbs, torso, head and neck. You may like to use an anatomy text book to learn/revise some of these areas or get a clearer sense of the direction of the muscle fibres and even the spiral patterns of the limb musculature connecting into the torso. You could also label the two diagrams that follow on. See appendix for some pre-labeled diagrams.

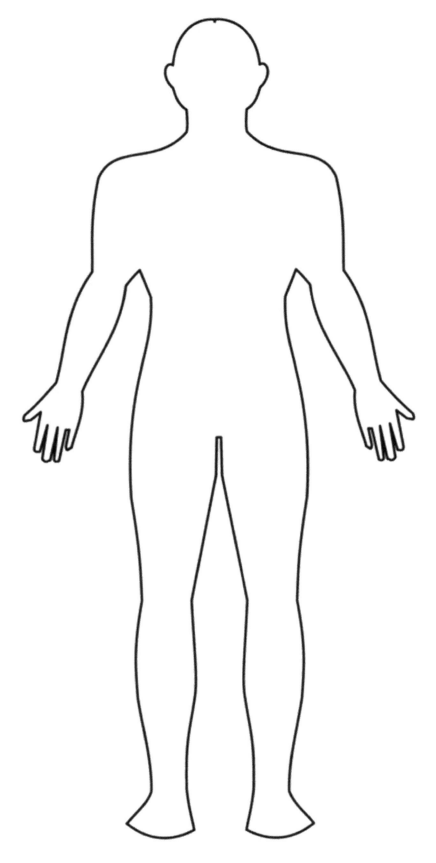

Fig. 150

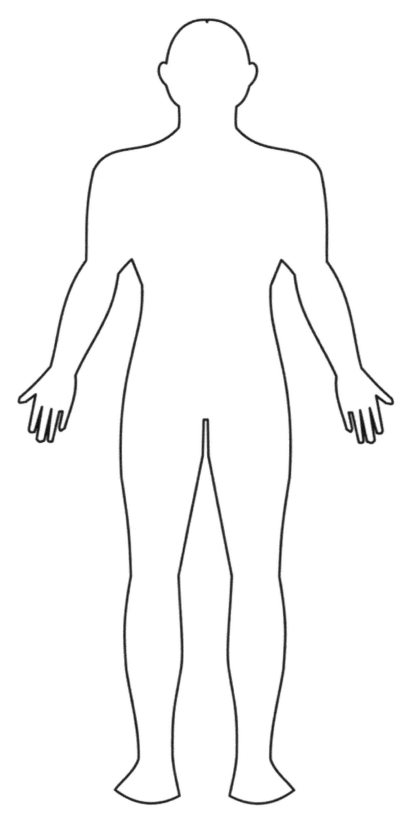

Fig. 151

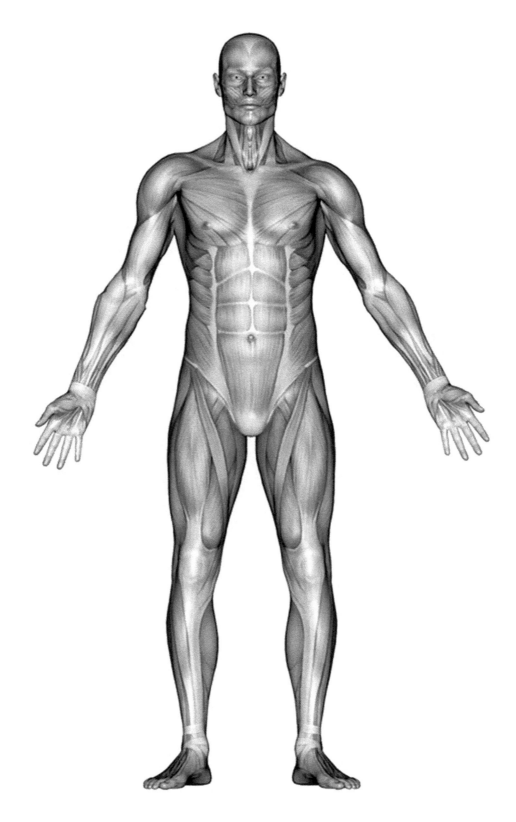

Fig. 152

150

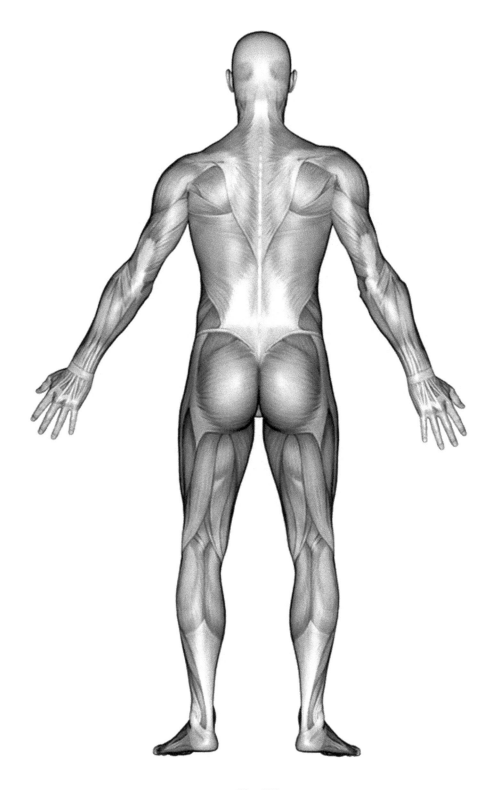

Fig. 153

Part Two

A New Map of You: Re-drawing and reviewing your Body Map

We have come to the point where it will be very informative for you to once again draw yourself, just as you did in Session One.

Before you do so, you may like to revise the following areas in sitting, standing or laying in semi supine.

✓ *The balance of your head on your spine at the Atlanto-Occipital (AO) joint*

✓ *The curves of the whole spine through its 24 individual vertebra*

✓ *The highly moveable, 24 individual ribs joining at the back with the spine and in front with the sternum*

✓ *The location and orientation of the diaphragm and lungs*

✓ *The whole arm with its 4 major joints starting with the sternoclavicular joint*

✓ *The pelvis through which weight is transferred into the legs in standing or the ischial tuberosities (sitting bones) in sitting*

✓ *The leg bones and the joints of the knees, ankles and feet that receive the incoming weight of the rest of the body and take the body into locomotion*

✓ *Structures of the head and neck including the jaw, larynx, hyoid bone and relational distance between eyes, ears, nose, lips, top of the head, TMJ joint.*

✓ *The internal organs and three dimensionality of the whole torso*

When you are ready you can 🗒 DRAW a Map/Diagram of your whole body on the following page.
ⓘ Remember this activity is not a test! Your drawing will provide an invaluable reference point and show you areas of your map you could continue to work on in the future.

(If you feel unable to draw from scratch, you may like to label to body outline also provided in this booklet. Simply draw and label as much detail as you can.)

152

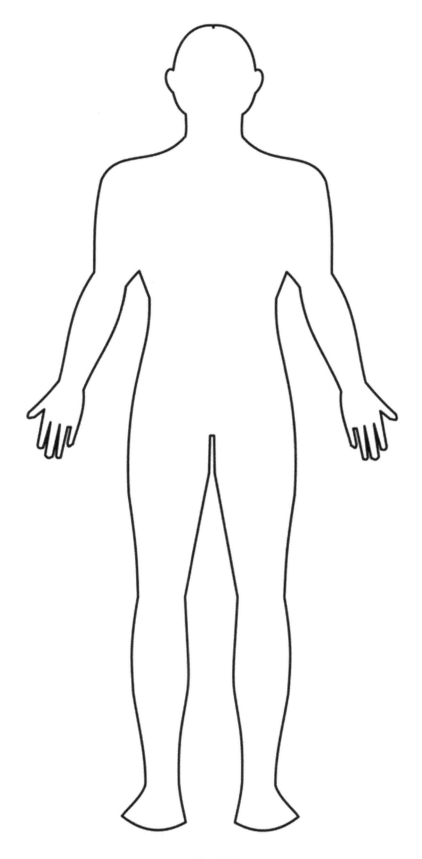

Fig. 154

Part Three

Practical applications to workplace and other activities

As you have been working through this unit you have most likely been considering the application of the things you are learning to your daily life, in particular your profession. This session, in consultation with your fellow learners and trainer, you will practically explore a number of real-life scenarios.

▤   Take a moment now to list a couple of scenarios you would like to look at with the group and under the guidance of your trainer.

Fig. 155

Fig. 156

Part Four

A review of Body Mapping processes and conclusions

⬜ RECALL the body mapping processes we have covered in this unit:

- ✓ Drawing
- ✓ Asking Questions i.e. where are my lungs?
- ✓ Looking at anatomical images (books, internet)
- ✓ Palpating (touch)
- ✓ Imitation (observing those who move well- babies, some elite sports people, dancers, martial artists)
- ✓ Looking in the mirror
- ✓ Constructive rest/semi supine (conscious constructive thinking, imagining, visualizing)
- ✓ Lessons with an Alexander technique teacher

We move in the way in which we think we are constructed (consciously or unconsciously).

❾ DISCUSS and ▤Note
With a partner, discuss what you have learned and experienced during this unit. Then, write down some areas that you intend to continue to work on and what of the above processes you will use.

APPENDICES

GLOSSARY

Directions: *These are the set of 'orders' that we can project in order to establish proper functioning of the Primary Control. "Allow the neck to be free so that the head can move forward and up so that the back can lengthen and widen."*

End gaining: *Going for one's end without attention upon the process of getting there.*

Inhibition: *Consciously preventing operating out of habit and so interfering with the Primary Control, often by stopping.*

Means-whereby: *Attending to the means-whereby is placing attention on the process rather than going straight for our end goal.*

Primary Control: *The dynamic relationship of our head, neck and back (torso).*

Self: *Human complex of body, mind and emotion.*

Unreliable/Faulty Sensory Appreciation: *Faulty perception, particularly of the kinesthetic sense, caused over time by misuse of ourselves.*

Use: *The way in which we do things or 'use ourselves' over which we can exercise choice.*

BIBLIOGRAPHY

Alexander, F.M. *Constructive Conscious Control of the Individual,* Mouritz, London, 1923 (2000).

Alexander, F.M. *Use of the Self,* London, Orion Books, 2001.

Allen, M., Malde, M., Zeller., Kurt Alexander. *What Every Singer Needs to Know About the Body,* San Diego, Plural Publishing, 2009.

Brennan, Richard. *Change Your Posture, Change Your Life: How the power of the Alexander Technique can combat back pain, tension and stress*, London, Watkins Publishing, 2012.

Calais-Germain, Blandine. *Anatomy of Movement*, Seattle, Eastland Press, 1999.

Conable, Barbara. *What Every Musician Needs to Know About the Body: The Practical Application of Body Mapping to Making Music*, Portland OR, Andover Press, 2000.

Dimon, Theodore Jr. *Anatomy of the Moving Body: A Basic Course in Bones, Muscles and Joints*, California, North Atlantic Books, 2008.

Franklin, Eric. *Dynamic Alignment Through Imagery*, Champaign USA, Human Kinetics, 1996.

Gelb, Michael. *Body Learning: An Introduction to the Alexander Technique,* London, Aurum Press, 1987.

Jones, Frank Pierce. *Collected Writings on the Alexander Technique,* Massachusetts, Alexander Technique Archives Inc., 1998.

Kapit W., Elson L.M., *The Anatomy Colouring Book,* USA, Benjamin Cummings Publishers, 2002.

Langford, Elizabeth. *Mind and Muscle,* Holand, Garant Publishing, 1999.

Macdonald, Patrick. *The Alexander Technique As I See It,* Bath, Bookcraft, 2002.

Olsen, Andrea. *Body Stories: A Guide to Experiential Anatomy*, New York, Station Hill Press, 1991.

Park, Glenn. *The Art of Changing: A New Approach to the Alexander Technique*, Bath, Ashgrove Press Limited, 1989.

Raff, Chris. *Introducing the Alexander Technique*, Australia, Axiom, 2011.

Todd, Mabel Elsworth. *The Thinking Body*, New York, Dance Horizons, 1977.

The Science of Body Mapping

To read about the *Science of Body Mapping* go to *Andover Educators* http://bodymap.org/main/?p=213 by T. Richard Nichols, Ph.D. (Departments of Physiology and Biomedical Engineering Emory University) [1]

Ideokinesis

Ideokinesis is an approach that engages visual and tactile-kinesthetic imagery to support the improvement of human posture and body movement. Ideokinesis works from the premise that visualizing movement only with the mind's eye (either as movement within the body or in space), without any perceivable sensation of muscular effort, primes neural pathways and reprograms unnecessary and unwanted muscular tensions. Fiona was first introduced to Ideokinesis during her tertiary dance training and classes with lecturer Wendy Smith.

Sports psychology research has shown that visualizing a clear goal of an action readily coordinates the neuromuscular details of the movement (the muscular recruitment, sequencing, and timing and force requirements). Physical practice combined with mental practice can lead to more improvement in motor performance and strength than either physical or mental practice alone. Further brain imaging technology reveals that mentally practicing a motor image utilizes the same brain regions as actual physical execution. Visualization, then, is a powerful tool in linking mind and body in programming or re-programming a "right" (intended) action without excessive wear-and-tear on the body from physical practice. In dance this is often referred to as, intelligent practice and can be effectively adopted in sports and music also.

Ideokinesis has been known by many names in its nearly 100-year history and is currently practiced primarily by individuals in the field of dance and somatics. The term Ideokinesis was applied to the discipline in the early 1970s and has become its most universally recognized title. You can learn more **at** http://www.ideokinesis.com

Practice Exam

Written test for Unit ATTMAP607A: Use Body-Mapping to improve movement and posture
Please use your own words to give short answers to the following:

1. What are the basic Alexander Directions for the Primary Control (dynamic organisation of head, neck and back)?

    _____
    _____
    _____
    _____

2. What is a 'Body Map' or what is 'Body Mapping'?

    _____
    _____
    _____

3. Why is an accurate 'Body Map' important?

    _____
    _____
    _____

4. What do we mean when we say 'accurate' Body Map? (*Location* of a joint is just one aspect of accuracy. What are some other aspects?)

    _____
    _____
    _____
    _____
    _____

5. List 5 tools/processes we can use to improve (clarify/refine) our own or our student' Body Map?

    _____
    _____
    _____
    _____
    _____

6. Name 2 common mis-mappings we may encounter as Alexander Technique teachers/teachers/body workers and beside these, how they will negatively impact upon a person's movement.

    _____
    _____
    _____

7. Describe 2 ways in which we may get a sense that a person has an area of their body mis-mapped

_____

_____

_____

_____

_____

8. During this Body Mapping course, you will have illuminated and explored some aspects of your own mapping. (a) Name one part of your Body Map that you have become aware of (because it was unclear/unrefined/non-existent) and (b) what processes have you engaged in order to improve this area of your Map?

(a) _____

_____

_____

(b) _____

_____

_____

_____

9. On this image of the base of the skull, label (a) the occipital condyles (where the top cervical vertebra (atlas) articulates with the skull (occiput) and (b) the HARD palette

10. What is the name of the FIRST joint of the arm (where the arm and body connect)?

_____

_____

11. On this diagram, use an arrow to indicate in which direction the diaphragm moves when we INHALE

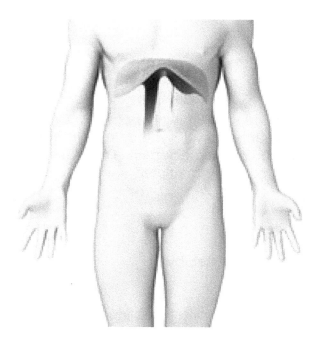

12. Describe the problem with how this picture diagrammatically represents the anatomy of our ankle joint. What would be a better way to draw this area, even as a stick figure? Draw this.

13. *Complete this sentence...*

Kinaesthesia (from kinema - movement and thesia - perception) is the perception or sense we have of

TMJ Dysfunction and Articles

TMJ Dysfunction

- Pain (at TMJ and headache, teeth, shoulders, neck)
- Restricted Movement
- Noise

It is hypothesized that there is a great deal of similarity between TMD and other pain syndromes like fibromyalgia, irritable bowel syndrome, interstitial cystitis, headache, chronic lower back pain and chronic neck pain. These disorders have also been theorized to be caused by centrally mediated sensitivity to pain, and furthermore they often occur together.

- **Central sensitivity syndromes**

- **Emotional stress** (causes and can be caused by)

- **Trauma**
  Trauma, both micro and macrotrauma, is sometimes identified as a possible cause of TMD, however the evidence is not strong. Prolonged mouth opening (hyper-extension) is also suggested as a possible cause. It is thought that this leads to microtrauma and subsequent muscular hyperactivity. This may occur during dental treatment, with oral intubation whilst under a general anesthetic, during singing or wind instrument practice (really these can be thought of as parafunctional activities). Damage may be incurred during violent yawning, laughing, road traffic accidents, sports injuries, interpersonal violence, or during dental treatment, (such as tooth extraction).

- **Occlusal factors**
  Occlusal factors as an etiologic factor in TMD is a controversial topic. Abnormalities of occlusion (problems with the bite) are often blamed for TMD but there is no evidence that these factors are involved. Occlusal abnormalities are incredibly common, and most people with occlusal abnormalities do not have TMD.

Some articles that may be of interest in relation to TMJ dysfunction and Central Sensitivity Syndromes:

http://www.ncbi.nlm.nih.gov/pmc/articles/PMC3052797/

http://www.maneyonline.com/doi/pdfplus/10.1179/1476830511Y.0000000017

http://books.google.com.au/books?hl=en&lr=&id=MMCTAgAAQBAJ&oi=fnd&pg=PP1&dq=mental+focus+and+chewing+gum&ots=R6SEn1X3RA&sig=QPW1Wwp DflSxS7M0Jjil7uYFDaQ#v=onepage&q&f=false

http://www.sciencedirect.com/science/article/pii/S0304394004002393

Foot Exercises from SESSION SIX, Part Three

Exercises for re-activating, mobilizing and strengthening the feet

Equipment: Chair, tennis ball, large felt marker pen or piece of wooden dowel

Set-Up:
- Sitting in a chair (a soft sofa is not ideal)
- Soles of the feet are flat on the floor in front of you
- Sitting so that your sitting bones (boney bits in your bottom) are in contact with the chair
- Project your Alexander Directions *allow the neck to be free so that the head can move forward and up so that the whole torso can lengthen and widen.* Repeatedly project these directions as you move through the exercises.

1. BALL UNDER THE FOOT: *place tennis ball under the foot and massage the plantar fascia (sole of foot) by rolling it around. As you do this notice the movement in the hip, knee and ankle joint of that leg. Ensure the foot not being used is still flat on the floor to provide support in sitting.*
2. FELT MARKER/DOWEL ROLL: *Repeat this same exercise, this time rolling the object along the length of the sole of the foot.*
3. MOVING AT THE ANKLE JOINT: *begin lifting the toes and ball of one foot off the ground, flexing at the ankle joint. As you lift the front of the foot up, the heel rests into the floor. The more you can think of the weight in the heel the more ease you will find in lifting the front of the foot. You want to avoid performing this action by engaging lots of muscular tension in the top of the foot and the shin area of your lower leg. Recall the mapping of the lower leg and foot as an upside down T rather than an L.*
4. CREASING AT THE TOE JOINTS: *lift the heel of one foot at a time while keeping the ball of the foot and toes on the floor such that you crease (have a look down if you need to) at the big toe joint and joints of the other toes too. Watch that as you do this the top of the foot is not pushing out to the side (overstretching the lateral/outside aspect of the foot) or pushing in (putting to much pressure through the big toe joint and overstretching medial/inside aspect of the foot).*
5. SEPARATE THE TOES: Cross one leg over to rest the foot on your thigh or in such a way that you can access your foot. (Remember to come forward and down to your foot using your hip joints rather than rounding the spine) *Place the fingers of the opposite hand to foot in the spaces between each toe. If this is not initially possible, simple hold the toes in such a way that you are lengthening them and encouraging them to separate.*
6. TORQUING THE FOOT: *Holding the same foot you have just separated the toes of, move the left and right halves of the foot in opposite directions, allowing movement at the ankle joint. You will notice there is a subtle torque in the movement that naturally takes place in our gait (walking) cycle.*

7. FIST TAPPING: *Make a fist with your hand and begin to pummel the sole, sides and top of the foot. As you do so you can imagine all 26 bones are being vibrated a little and you are 'waking up' the foot.*
8. STANDING BRUSHING: *Standing on one foot (holding on to a chair for balance) brush the sole of the foot along the floor (thinking of a 'licking' action) using a cycling motion through the whole leg.*
9. STANDING POINT ANF FLEX: *Standing on one foot (holding on to a chair for balance) rest the heel into the ground and flex the toes up towards you. You may feel a stretch and opening through the back of the lower leg and the sole of the foot. Then, reverse this movement to point the toes into the floor (like a ballerina).*
10. FOOT TOP STRETCH: *Standing side on to and holding a chair, stretch the top of each foot by pointing the foot, bending the knee and resting some weight through the top of the foot. Try not to scrunch the toes and aim instead to have the top of the foot in contact with the floor.*
11. STANDING ON ONE FOOT: Standing on one foot *Practice standing on one foot at a time. Allow the micro shifts to happen (rather than resisting them by tightening). If in doing this your foot seems to flatten/roll in think about "don't squash the mouse". If you find you roll out to the side of the foot, think about anchoring the big toe.*
12. CALF AND ACHILLES STRETCHES: *Stand square on facing the back of a chair and hold on lightly for balance. Step back one foot and bend the front knee to come into a small lunge. Keep both feet flat on the floor and look down to check the toes of both feet are still facing straight ahead. Bend the front knee until you feel a stretch in the calf/Achilles area of the back leg. Then straighten both legs and change to bending the back knee and allow most of the weight to shift into the back foot. You are looking for a sense of opening in the Achilles area and are working with deep flexion at the front of the ankle.*
13. RISING UP: *Stand on two feet, shift the weight into the fronts of the feet so much so that you can begin to lift the heels off the ground to rise up onto the balls of the feet (remembering to crease at the toe joints and lengthen the toes). You may also like to raise the arms up in front of you.*

Choosing Footwear:

1. *Flexibility of the shoe, in particular the sole. Does it bend and where does it bend?*
2. *Height of the heel. Does it have a heel? If it is flat, does it have enough cushioning?*
3. *Internal space. Is there space for your foot inside the shoe? In particular, can the toes spread in the toe box area?*
4. *Weight of the shoe. How heavy is it and how does this feel not only in your hand but also on your foot? Will the weight of the shoe fatigue your legs if you are walking for a long time?*

Full Unit Description

ATTMAP607A   **Use body mapping to improve movement and posture**

Unit Descriptor   This unit of competency describes the basic knowledge of body mapping to the level required to identify body mapping issues both in students' own use and that of their students/clients in the context of Alexander Technique teaching, health care work or teaching a skill.

This unit is included in the group of units required for teacher accreditation with AUSTAT.

Employability Skills   This unit contains Employability Skills.

Application of the Unit   The application of knowledge and skills described in this competency unit may relate to functions such as client questioning and assessment using body mapping.

Functions at this level require a broad overview of the coordinated functioning of the human body and common body mapping errors associated with defects in this coordination.

This unit application has been developed to be applied in a range of workplaces where teachers are training students or clients in a wide range of physical skills or activities or in a range of clinical situations where therapists are treating clients or advising them on postural and movement issues.

This unit will not cover hands on Alexander technique teaching skills.

ELEMENT	PERFORMANCE CRITERIA
Elements describe the essential outcomes of a unit of competency.	*Performance criteria describe the required performance needed to demonstrate achievement of the element. Where bold italicised text is used, further information is detailed in the required skills and knowledge and/or the range statement. Assessment of performance is to be consistent with the evidence guide.*

1	Analyse the coordination of the healthy musculo-skeletal system in activity	1.1	Describe the normal function, structure, location and use of ***the major joints*** of the human body and their ***movement possibilities***
		1.2	Explain the relationship of the Alexander Technique theory of the ***primary control*** to ***body mapping***
		1.3	Identify the ***healthy and coordinated relationship between the different parts of the body***
		1.4	Demonstrate the healthy and coordinated relationship between the different parts of the body required to improve the use of the self

2	Apply basic knowledge of body mapping in a way that supports the healthy musculo-skeletal system in activity	2.1	Model good use to **clients**/students by applying a basic understanding of how to maintain own body in a state of improved coordination
		2.2	Work with a basic understanding of the relationships between body parts required to support improved coordination when teaching/treating students/clients
		2.3	Provide feedback and information to students/clients in order to assist them to correct body mapping errors

REQUIRED SKILLS AND KNOWLEDGE

This describes the essential skills and knowledge and their level, required for this unit.

The following essential skills must be assessed as part of this unit

- Literacy skills sufficient to read and understand anatomy text books
- Basic or developing clinical or teaching skills in a specific therapy or discipline
- Use and articulate accurately anatomical and common terminology for structures which are important for body mapping
- Apply essential knowledge as outlined in own work role

The following knowledge must be assessed as part of this unit

- An overview of the theory of body mapping
- A beginning understanding of Alexander Technique principles
- Common body mapping errors
- The muscles and joints associated with body mapping errors
- The primary control
- Healthy breathing and vocal production
- Common body mapping errors related to specific activities
- Relationship of body mapping to the Alexander Technique

RANGE STATEMENT

The range statement relates to the unit of competency as a whole. It allows for different work environments and situations that may affect performance. Bold italicised wording in the Performance Criteria is detailed below. Add any essential operating conditions that may be present with training and assessment depending on the work situation, needs of the candidate, accessibility of the item, and local industry and regional contexts.

the major joints must include but are not limited to:	Atlanto-occipital joint
	Joints of the spine
	Joints of the shoulder girdle
	Hip joint
	Knee joint
	Shoulder girdle
	Wrist
	Ankle joint
movement possibilities refers to:	Healthy range of movement of the joints
primary control refers to	Relationship between the head, neck, torso and rest of the body
body mapping refers to	Teaching and learning accurate anatomical and movement information at a cognitive and experiential level
healthy and coordinated relationship between the different parts of the body refers to:	The balanced relationship of all the joints from the head to the feet
clients may refer to	Alexander Technique students
	Clients of therapists
	Students who are learning a skill in individual or group classes e.g. yoga, dance, tai chi, swimming, singing, acting, public speaking – any physical activity which requires skill development

EVIDENCE GUIDE

The evidence guide provides advice on assessment and must be read in conjunction with the Performance Criteria, Required Skills and Knowledge, the Range Statement and the Assessment Guidelines for this unit.

Overview of Assessment	A person who demonstrates competency in this unit must demonstrate the essential knowledge and skills required to be able to perform the outcomes described in the Elements to the required level listed in the performance criteria. Assessment must be referenced to and informed by the range statement.
Critical aspects for assessment and evidence required to demonstrate competency in this unit	Evidence should be collected over a considerable period of time in a range of actual or simulated environments for demonstration of knowledge and skills.
	Evidence that the Alexander technique and body-mapping principles have been applied to improving the trainee's use of the self, in order to be able to teach, communicate, demonstrate and model body mapping to clients/students
	Apply knowledge within the requirements of the work role
	Consistently apply knowledge over the required range of workplace applications relevant to an identified work role
Context of and specific resources for assessment	Assessment should replicate workplace conditions as far as possible.
	Where, for reasons of safety, assessment takes place away from the workplace, simulations should be used to represent workplace conditions as closely as possible.
	Resources for assessment may include access to materials and space as required to demonstrate competence, such as:
	Anatomical models, charts and/or diagrams
	Whiteboard
	Text books
	Relevant technology, e.g. Internet, PowerPoint
	Workplace or simulated work environment

Method of assessment	Assessment must include:

Questioning (verbal and written) to address Essential Knowledge as outlined in this unit

Observation of the demonstrated application of body mapping principles in student's use of self

Observation of student giving body mapping information in real or simulated work environment

Written test

This unit may be assessed as a stand-alone unit. It may also be holistically assessed along with the following units:

ATTASS602A Assess a student from an Alexander Technique perspective

ATTGRO605A Teach the Alexander Technique to a group

ATTIND604A Teach the Alexander Technique to an individual

ATTSPE606A Teach the Alexander Technique in a specialist area

HLTAP301 Recognise healthy body systems in a health care context

HLTCOM408B Use specific health terminology to communicate effectively

HLTCOM404C Communicate effectively with clients

ATTSEL608A Use the Alexander Technique for self care in clinical and/or teaching practice

Attributions for photos and illustrations

Fig. 1 Isobel Knowles © Einstein's Moon

SECTION ONE
Fig. 2 Wiktoria Pawlak/Shutterstock
Fig. 3 BarsRsind/Shutterstock
Fig. 4 Moriz/Shutterstock
Fig. 5 Jaroma/Shutterstock
Fig. 6 skyhawk x/Shutterstock
Fig. 7 Ben Schonewille/Shutterstock
Fig. 8 Stihii/Shutterstock
Fig. 9 Sebastian Kaulitzki/Shutterstock
Fig. 10 Sebastian Kaulitzki/Shutterstock
Fig. 11 Sebastian Kaulitzki/Shutterstock
Fig. 12 Fiona Bryant © Einstein's Moon
Fig. 13 Fiona Bryant © Einstein's Moon
Fig. 14 Fiona Bryant © Einstein's Moon
Fig. 15 Fiona Bryant © Einstein's Moon
Fig. 16 ostill/ Shutterstoc
Fig. 17 ostill/ Shutterstoc
Fig. 18 decade3d - anatomy online/ Shutterstock
Fig. 19 Alex Mit/Shutterstock
Fig. 20 Isobel Knowles © Einstein's Moon
Fig. 21 Isobel Knowles © Einstein's Moon

SECTION TWO
Fig. 22 Sebastian Kaulitzki/Shutterstock
Fig. 23 CLIPAREA l Custom media/Shutterstock
Fig. 24 Sebastian Kaulitzki/Shutterstock
Fig. 25 Tewan Banditrukkanka/Shutterstock
Fig. 26 Sebastian Kaulitzki/Shutterstock
Fig. 27 Sebastian Kaulitzki/Shutterstock
Fig. 28 Mannan Rao © Einstein's Moon
Fig. 29 Mannan Rao © Einstein's Moon
Fig. 30 Magic mine/Shutterstock
Fig. 31 Alila Medical Media/Shutterstock
Fig. 32 Sebastian Kaulitzki/Shutterstock
Fig. 33 Mannan Rao © Einstein's Moon

SECTION THREE
Fig. 34 3drenderings/Shutterstock
Fig. 35 Fiona Bryant © Einstein's Moon
Fig. 36 Sebastian Kaulitzki/Shutterstock
Fig. 37 Sebastian Kaulitzki/Shutterstock
Fig. 38 Alexilusmedical/Shutterstock
Fig. 39 Fiona Bryant © Einstein's Moon
Fig. 40 Fiona Bryant © Einstein's Moon
Fig. 41 Sebastian Kaulitzki/Shutterstock
Fig. 42 Sementer/Shutterstock
Fig. 43 Sebastian Kaulitzki/Shutterstock
Fig. 44 Fiona Bryant © Einstein's Moon
Fig. 45 Fiona Bryant © Einstein's Moon
Fig. 46 Fiona Bryant © Einstein's Moon
Fig. 47 Fiona Bryant © Einstein's Moon
Fig. 48 Fiona Bryant © Einstein's Moon
Fig. 49 Sebastian Kaulitzki/Shutterstock
Fig. 50 Africa Studio/Shutterstock
Fig. 51 Ostil/Shutterstock
Fig. 52 Alenavlad/Shutterstock

SECTION FOUR
Fig. 53 Santibhavank P/Shutterstock
Fig. 54 udaix/Shutterstock
Fig. 55 Alila Medical Media/Shutterstock
Fig. 56 Africa Studio/Shutterstock
Fig. 57 Fiona Bryant © Einstein's Moon
Fig. 58 Fiona Bryant © Einstein's Moon
Fig. 59 Shutterstock
Fig. 60 vadim kozlovsky/Shutterstock
Fig. 61 3drenderings/Shutterstock
Fig. 62 Alila Medical Media/Shutterstock
Fig. 63 vadim kozlovsky/Shutterstoc
Fig. 64 Fiona Bryant © Einstein's Moon
Fig. 65 Fiona Bryant © Einstein's Moon
Fig. 66 Africa Studio/Shutterstock
Fig. 67 Alenavlad/Shutterstock
Fig. 68 Alenavlad/Shutterstock

SECTION FIVE
Fig. 69 Sebastian Kaulitzki/Shutterstock
Fig. 70 Maya2008/Shutterstock
Fig. 71 Sebastian Kaulitzki/Shutterstoc
Fig. 72 Sebastian Kaulitzki/Shutterstoc
Fig. 73 Fiona Bryant © Einstein's Moon
Fig. 74 Fiona Bryant © Einstein's Moon
Fig. 75 Sebastian Kaulitzki/Shutterstock
Fig. 76 Oleksii Natykach/Shutterstock
Fig. 77 goa novi/Shutterstock
Fig. 78 Fiona Bryant © Einstein's Moon
Fig. 79 Pavel L Photo and Video/Shutterstock
Fig. 80 Syda Productions/Shutterstock
Fig. 81 Sebastian Kaulitzki/Shutterstock
Fig. 82 Sebastian Kaulitzki/Shutterstock
Fig. 83 © Einstein's Moon
Fig. 84 © Einstein's Moon
Fig. 85 Fiona Bryant © Einstein's Moon
Fig. 86 Fiona Bryant © Einstein's Moon
Fig. 87 Sebastian Kaulitzki/Shutterstock
Fig. 88 Sebastian Kaulitzki/Shutterstock
Fig. 89 Sebastian Kaulitzki/Shutterstock
Fig. 90 Fiona Bryant © Einstein's Moon
Fig. 91 Sebastian Kaulitzki/Shutterstock
Fig. 92 Fiona Bryant © Einstein's Moon

SECTION SIX
Fig. 93 Hannah Ensor/Shutterstock
Fig. 94 skyhawk x/Shutterstoc
Fig. 95 Sebastian Kaulitzki/Shutterstock
Fig. 96 Fiona Bryant © Einstein's Moon
Fig. 97 Fiona Bryant © Einstein's Moon
Fig. 98 BioMedical/Shutterstock
Fig. 99 skyhawk x/Shutterstoc
Fig. 100 Wavebreakmedia/Shutterstock
Fig. 101 Sebastian Kaulitzki/Shutterstock
Fig. 102 Fiona Bryant © Einstein's Moon
Fig. 103 Fiona Bryant © Einstein's Moon
Fig. 104 AkeSak/Shutterstock
Fig. 105 Sebastian Kaulitzki/Shutterstock
Fig. 106 zeffir/Shutterstock
Fig. 107 Julenochek/Shutterstock

SECTION SEVEN
Fig. 108 Fiona Bryant © Einstein's Moon
Fig. 109 Andrey_Popov/Shutterstock
Fig. 110 Zurijeta/Shutterstock
Fig. 111 szefei/Shutterstock
Fig. 112 Shop hylyte/Shutterstock
Fig. 113 Fiona Bryant © Einstein's Moon

SECTION EIGHT
Fig. 114 Nerthuz/Shutterstock
Fig. 115 Designua/Shutterstock
Fig. 116 stihii/Shutterstock
Fig. 117 Alila Medical Media/Shutterstock
Fig. 118 Fiona Bryant © Einstein's Moon
Fig. 119 Fiona Bryant © Einstein's Moon
Fig. 120 Fiona Bryant © Einstein's Moon
Fig. 121 Fiona Bryant © Einstein's Moon
Fig. 122 Jaroma/Shutterstock
Fig. 123 Jaroma/Shutterstock
Fig. 124 Fiona Bryant © Einstein's Moon
Fig. 125 Fiona Bryant © Einstein's Moon
Fig. 126 szefei/Shutterstock
Fig. 127 nikitabuida/Shutterstock
Fig. 128 Ollyy/Shutterstock
Fig. 129 CLIPAREA I Custom media/Shutterstock
Fig. 130 u3d/Shutterstock
Fig. 131 u3d/Shutterstock
Fig. 132 Nerthuz/Shutterstock
Fig. 133 u3d/Shutterstock
Fig. 134 u3d/Shutterstock
Fig. 135 u3d/Shutterstock

SECTION NINE
Fig. 136 Jaroma/Shutterstock
Fig. 137 Sebastian Kaulitzki/Shutterstock
Fig. 138 Stihii/Shutterstock
Fig. 139 Sebastian Kaulitzki/Shutterstock
Fig. 140 Chris Harvey/Shutterstock
Fig. 141 Medical Art Inc/Shutterstock
Fig. 142 Ben Schonewille/Shutterstock
Fig. 143 Alila Medical Media/Shutterstock
Fig. 144 Christian Bertrand/Shutterstock
Fig. 145 Isobel Knowles © Einstein's Moon
Fig. 146 Copyright: Sebastian Kaulitzki

SECTION TEN
Fig. 147 Wiktoria Pawlak/Shutterstock
Fig. 148 Sebastian Kaulitzki/Shutterstoc
Fig. 149 Alila Medical Media/Shutterstoc
Fig. 150 Wiktoria Pawlak/Shutterstock
Fig. 151 Wiktoria Pawlak/Shutterstock
Fig. 152 ecliptic blue/Shutterstock
Fig. 153 ecliptic blue/Shutterstock
Fig. 154 Wiktoria Pawlak/Shutterstock
Fig. 155 freelanceartist/Shutterstock
Fig. 156 ostill/Shutterstock

Printed in Australia
AUHW011155070520
327153AU00021B/940

9 780994 262523